ATOMIC-ABSORPTION
SPECTROPHOTOMETRY

ATOMIC-ABSORPTION
SPECTROPHOTOMETRY

By

W. T. ELWELL, F.R.I.C.

and

J. A. F. GIDLEY, B.Sc., A.Inst.P.

Analytical Section Research Department
I. C. I. Metals Division
Birmingham, England

THE MACMILLAN COMPANY

NEW YORK

1962

The Macmillan Company
60 Fifth Avenue, New York 11, N.Y.

Brett-Macmillan Ltd.
132 Water Street South, Galt,
Ontario, Canada

Pergamon Press Ltd.
Headington Hill Hall, Oxford
4 & 5 Fitzroy Square, London, W.1

Library of Congress Card Number 61-18493

Set in Monotype Imprint 11 on 13 point and printed in Great Britain at
THE ALDEN PRESS, OXFORD

CONTENTS

The authors are grateful to Dr. A. C. Menzies and Mr. M. Milbourn for criticisms and suggestions made in the course of preparing this publication, and to Mr. L. E. Tavender for checking the proofs.

CHAPTER 1

INTRODUCTION

SINCE the end of the Second World War there has been an increasing interest in impurities, present in the parts per million range, in certain materials. It is true that problems associated with trace impurities in metals have been with us almost since the time of the first metal preparations by prehistoric men and only the definition of "trace" has changed with time. This interest has been sustained, largely by an improved knowledge of the metallurgical significance of trace constituents, although, in some fields, there has been a change in emphasis and specified elements are undesirable, and occasionally desirable, for entirely different reasons. This is typified in the field of nuclear engineering where elements with high neutron cross-section absorption, or long half-life periods, are undesirable, consequently specifications for these constructional materials limit these elements to parts, or even fractional parts, per million of the parent metal.

In other analytical fields there has been, and still is, a growing importance in the determination of trace constituents, e.g. in agriculture, biology and industrial trade effluents. In dealing with such materials the analyst has a difficult problem, and gone are the days when an analytical report which simply stated "trace" or "not detected" would be acceptable. How then are these current problems solved?

Over the past twenty years there have been rapid advances in the inorganic field of analytical chemistry, including the development of improved colorimetric procedures and superior spectrophotometers for determining optical densities of coloured solutions at narrowly defined wavelengths. Now, commonplace among the analyst's professional tools, are polarography, emission spectrometry, X-ray fluorescence, and a glance at the index column of any of the leading English or American journals of analytical chemistry will indicate the extent to which this list of instrumental methods could be extended, and is likely to be extended, with the advent of new techniques.

The development of physical methods of analysis has been brought about by a fundamental study, and appreciation, of atomic or molecular characteristics, and the practical interpretation achieved by a combination of effort by the physicist and chemist, each making their specialized contribution.

When a new physico-chemical procedure is proposed, the analyst produces a list of stereotyped questions relating to such aspects as specificity, sensitivity, speed, inter-element effects, "blanks" and the provision of standards.

Atomic-absorption spectrophotometry does not provide completely favourable answers to all of these questions, but this new analytical technique has many commendable features and useful applications, especially where trace amounts of certain metals are to be determined.

In the following pages an attempt has been made to bring the reader up to date with developments in those fields of analysis in which atomic-absorption spectrophotometry has, or is likely to have, useful applications. Because limitations of the technique are equally important, this aspect has also received due attention and comment.

No single instrumental method of analysis is capable of solving all of the analyst's problems; the authors' objectives, therefore, have been to present available information in perspective but, because of the increasing interest in this relatively simple, though none the less reliable, analytical technique, it is appreciated that rapid developments are being made, and current information will soon become out-dated.

CHAPTER 2

THEORY

IN emission spectroscopy the extent to which the emission due to an element is influenced by the presence of a second element (inter-element effects) can be troublesome.

For analytical work of the highest precision, involving the use of photo-electric direct-reading spectrometers, it is essential to calibrate the instrument at frequent intervals, using standards with compositions and history, similar to those of the samples under examination. [1] The provision of a suitable range of appropriate standards can present a problem, the necessity of which is illustrated in a report by Prokof'ev, [2] who comments that, in the spark spectrum, for the same concentration of silicon, the intensity of silicon lines in brass is an eighth of that in steel; the intensity of the corresponding lines in aluminium alloys is even less.

A satisfactory explanation of these variable effects in arc or spark discharges, has not yet been given, because the method of excitation in these light sources is so complex that a completely theoretical approach to this problem is exceedingly difficult. The observation that inter-element effects are of the same order of magnitude for different lines, due to the same element, corresponding to transitions between different energy states, indicates that they probably arise from variations in atomic-vapour concentration rather than changes in excitation conditions.

In an attempt to devise a spectrochemical procedure free from these inter-element effects, Walsh [3] examined possible causes of interference.

3

Changes in atomic vapour concentration of the elements being determined can be brought about in several ways, including a variation in the volatilization rate of the sample, chemical composition of the parent material and changes in temperature of the discharge. Walsh considered only the effect of variation of discharge temperature and examined the effects of changes in temperature on atomic vapour in thermal equilibrium.

The intensity of emission of a spectrum line due to the transition from an excited state, j, of excitation energy, E_j, to the ground state of zero energy is proportional to the number of atoms, N_j, in the excited state; neglecting any effects caused by self-absorption and induced emission. N_j is related to the number of atoms in the ground state, N_0, by the equation:

$$N_j = N_0 \frac{P_j}{P_0} \exp-(E_j/kT)$$

where P_j and P_0 are the statistical weights for the excited state and ground state respectively.

The magnitude of N_j/N_0 is illustrated in Table 1, where the calculated values[3] for resonance lines of various elements are given.

TABLE 1.

VALUES OF N_j/N_0 FOR VARIOUS RESONANCE LINES

Resonance lines	N_j/N_0			
	$T = 2000°K$	$T = 3000°K$	$T = 4000°K$	$T = 5000°K$
Cs 8521 Å	$4·44 \times 10^{-4}$	$7·24 \times 10^{-3}$	$2·98 \times 10^{-2}$	$6·82 \times 10^{-2}$
Na 5890 Å	$9·86 \times 10^{-6}$	$5·88 \times 10^{-4}$	$4·44 \times 10^{-3}$	$1·51 \times 10^{-2}$
Ca 4227 Å	$1·21 \times 10^{-7}$	$3·69 \times 10^{-5}$	$6·03 \times 10^{-4}$	$3·33 \times 10^{-3}$
Zn 2139 Å	$7·29 \times 10^{-15}$	$5·58 \times 10^{-10}$	$1·48 \times 10^{-7}$	$4·32 \times 10^{-6}$

(*Reproduced by kind permission of the Editors of Spectrochimica Acta*)

In most instances, it will be seen that the number of atoms in the lowest excited state is very small compared with the number of atoms in the ground state, and the ratio only becomes appreciable at high temperatures and in transitions resulting in resonance lines of long wavelengths. The strongest resonance lines of most elements lie below 6000 Å and, because we are mainly concerned with atomic vapours at temperatures below 3000°K, the fraction N_j/N_0 will be very small and N_j negligible compared with N_0. Because the fraction of atoms in higher energy levels than E_j is even smaller, ΣN_j will still be negligible compared with N_0, and N_0 will thus be equal to the total number of atoms, N. Whilst, therefore, the number of excited atoms varies exponentially with temperature, the number of atoms in the ground state will remain virtually constant.

If we now consider a parallel beam of radiation of intensity, I_0, at frequency ν, incident on an atomic vapour of thickness l cm, then if I_ν is the intensity of the transmitted radiation, the absorption coefficient, K_ν, of the vapour at frequency ν, is defined by the relation:

$$I_\nu = I_0 \exp-(K_\nu l)$$

The value of K_ν will vary with ν, since the absorption line has a finite width but, according to classical dispersion theory, the integrated absorption ($\int K_\nu d\nu$) is given by the relation:

$$\int K_\nu d\nu = \frac{\pi e^2}{mc} N_\nu f$$

where e is the electronic charge, m the electronic mass, c the velocity of light, N_ν the number of atoms/cm³ capable of absorbing radiation of frequency ν, and f the oscillator strength, i.e. the average number of electrons per atom capable of being excited by the incident radiation. Thus, for a transition initiated from the ground state, where N_ν is for practical purposes equal to N_0 (the total number of atoms per cm³), the integrated absorption is proportional to the concentration of free atoms in the absorbing medium and is independent of the temperature of the vapour.

There remains, however, a very severe problem, namely how

to measure the integrated absorption. At temperatures between 2000 and 3000°K, the width of an absorption line is about 0·02 Å. The factors that establish the line width are:

(a) The natural width of the line.

(b) Doppler broadening due to movements of the atoms relative to the observer.

(c) Pressure broadening due to the presence of neighbouring atoms (when broadening is due to atoms of the same kind as those absorbing radiation, this is known as resonance broadening).

(d) Stark broadening due to external electric fields or charged particles.

The natural width of the line (of the order of 10^{-4} Å) may be neglected in relation to the other factors. Doppler broadening is the main factor if the atomic vapour is produced in a low pressure furnace, such as that used by King;[4] both Doppler and pressure broadening occur in flame sources, as used in flame photometry, and all three variables, Doppler, pressure and stark broadening, are associated with conventional spectrographic arc and spark excitation sources.

To measure the profile of an absorption line accurately, and thereby obtain the integrated absorption, it is necessary to use an optical instrument with a resolution of 500,000, which is well beyond the capabilities of most spectrographs. The method of measurement suggested by Walsh is simple and effective and eliminates the need for a high resolution instrument. By using a sharp line source which emits lines with a much smaller half width than the absorption line, the absorption coefficient at the centre of the line can be measured. It has been shown[5] that if the shape of the absorption line is completely determined by Doppler broadening, then:

$$K_{max} = \frac{2\lambda^2}{D_\lambda} \sqrt{\left(\frac{\log_e 2}{\pi}\right)} \frac{\pi e^2}{mc^2} Nf$$

where K_{max} is the absorption coefficient at the centre of the line and D_λ is the Doppler line width. D_λ is proportional to $T^{\frac{1}{2}}$, hence K_{max} does not vary significantly with small changes in temperature and there remains a linear relation between absorption and concentration of free atoms in the absorbing medium. With such a sharp-line source, it is not necessary to use an instrument capable of high resolution to determine the absorption. The only requirement is the ability to separate a selected line from all other lines emitted by the source, and an instrument with a resolution comparable with that obtained by simple spectrographic equipment is satisfactory. Instrumental requirements for both source and measuring equipment will be dealt with in more detail later.

The most favoured method of obtaining an atomic vapour is to atomize a solution containing the element into a flame. Under these conditions, the presence of gases, other than the vapourized sample, will cause pressure broadening. This will be a constant factor, independent of sample concentration, and will cause a constant proportional lowering of K_{max}; however, the linear relation between concentration and absorption will be maintained but the sensitivity of the method will be reduced. When the concentration of the sample vapour is increased, the increased partial pressure of the atomic vapour will produce resonance broadening with a corresponding reduction in absorption. This reduction will not be a linear function of atomic vapour concentration and hence will destroy the linear relation between concentration and absorption, resulting in curvature of the calibration graph towards the concentration axis.

Other causes of graph curvature are discussed by Menzies.[6] If some of the light measured by the photocell does not undergo absorption in the flame, this will result in a curved calibration graph. If i_0 is the intensity of unabsorbed light then the measured optical density will be

$$\log \frac{I_0 + i_0}{I + i_0} \quad \text{instead of} \quad \log \frac{I_0}{I},$$

and the calibration graph will be asymptotic to the value

$$\log \frac{I_0 + i_0}{i_0},$$

instead of infinity. Unabsorbed light, or its equivalent, may arise in a variety of ways but in many instances suitable corrections can be applied. Photocell dark-current, scattered light in a monochromator, and light by-passing the flame are all instrumental factors which can be minimized. If the source of sharp-line radiation emits a relatively high intensity background continuum (cf. manganese, page 79) or an emission line close in wavelength to the absorption line (cf. iron, page 81) then it may be difficult to eliminate the effect. Various methods which may be used to reduce this effect of the unabsorbed light are described later.

From the foregoing theoretical considerations, it will be seen that measurement of atomic-absorption spectra should be less susceptible to inter-element effects than those observed in emission spectra, because any effect observed in the latter, due to variation in distribution of atoms over various excited states, is negligible in absorption spectra. Similarly, absorption will not be critically dependent on temperature, because the peak absorption coefficient varies with $T^{-\frac{1}{2}}$, whereas small changes in temperature cause large changes in emission intensity. This statement does not imply that no inter-element interferences occur in atomic-absorption procedures because, as mentioned earlier (page 4), the effect of temperature is only one of several possible causes of inter-element interferences.

CHAPTER 3

EQUIPMENT

ESSENTIAL requirements for atomic-absorption spectrophotometry include (a) sharp-line source, (b) means for vaporizing samples, (c) wavelength selector and (d) intensity measurement and recording equipment.

One experimental difficulty, which has caused a wide variation in the equipment used by different investigators, is the emission of light by the atomic vapour at the same resonance wavelength as that used for absorption measurements. Various methods of overcoming this difficulty will be described in the following sub-sections which deal more fully with major requirements.

3.1 SHARP-LINE SOURCE

Ideally a sharp-line source should emit resonance radiation of the element under examination with a line half-width considerably less than the Doppler width of the absorbing line, with sufficiently intense stable radiation to enable measurements to be made accurately. Several common light sources can be eliminated immediately, because they do not satisfy these requirements; e.g. normal spectrographic arcs, sparks or flame sources. Emission sources which can be, or have been, used include Geissler tubes, vapour discharge lamps, high-frequency electrodeless discharge and hollow-cathode lamps.

Geissler tubes are simple low-pressure discharge tubes containing vapour of the element to be excited. Although no mention of Geissler tubes appears to have been made in literature on atomic-absorption spectrophotometry, these tubes have been used for the investigation of fine structure of spectrum lines of various elements; for example, Tolansky[7] used Geissler tubes in his examination of the spark spectrum of arsenic. These tubes are best suited for the excitation of gases or materials with appreciable vapour pressures at fairly low temperatures and it is often an advantage to use them in conjunction with an auxiliary gas (e.g. neon or argon), to carry the discharge, so that the vapour pressure of the material to be excited is kept sufficiently low to reduce resonance broadening.

Laboratory vapour discharge lamps are commercially available, containing elements such as sodium, potassium, thallium, rubidium, caesium, mercury, cadmium, and zinc, and these may be used as light sources. Cadmium and zinc radiations

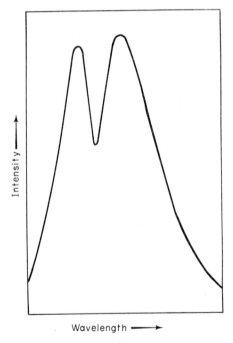

FIG. 1. Contour of Cd 2288 Å line emitted by Wotan lamp
at recommended current

(*Reproduced by kind permission of the Editors of* Spectrochimica Acta)

may be obtained more conveniently from hollow-cathode lamps but, for the other elements listed, vapour discharge lamps are probably the best source of radiation. When these lamps are operated at the recommended current, the emitted resonance lines exhibit considerable self-reversal. This was demonstrated by Russell, Shelton and Walsh,[8] who made a microphotometer trace of an echelle spectrum of the Cd 2288 Å line emitted by a Wotan lamp at the recommended current.

Walsh and his co-workers state that it was necessary to run a sodium lamp at 0·8 amp, instead of the recommended 1·3 amp, in order to remove self-reversal. The effect of reducing the current in a vapour discharge lamp is to reduce the temperature and vapour pressure of the metal vapour, thus reducing Doppler broadening, self-reversal and resonance broadening, all factors which would increase the sensitivity of the atomic-absorption procedure. This has been demonstrated in the authors' laboratory by measuring the absorption produced by 5 ppm of sodium in solution, at varying lamp operating currents. Results are shown in Table 2.

Although manufacturers of these vapour discharge-lamps

TABLE 2.

ABSORPTION PRODUCED BY 5 PPM SODIUM AT VARIOUS LAMP OPERATING CURRENTS

Current (amp)	Optical density
1·26*	0·055
1·00	0·105
0·81	0·135
0·71	0·150
0·59	0·195
0·50	0·215
0·40	0·225
0·31	0·215

*Manufacturer's recommended current

issue a warning against running at a lower current than that recommended, it was not observed that such treatment in any way harmed the tube; this is also borne out by other workers.[8]

There is no record of the use of high-frequency electrodeless discharge tubes in atomic-absorption spectrophotometry, but this important method of producing sharp-line spectra might be used with advantage in a study of the behaviour of elements such as mercury, cadmium, thallium, zinc and bismuth. Full details of the construction and operation of discharge lamps of this type are given elsewhere.[9, 10] Walsh and his co-workers[8] claim, however, that the light output from high-frequency electrodeless lamps is not as constant as that from hollow-cathode lamps.

The most useful and most used source for sharp resonance lines is the hollow-cathode lamp. These lamps can be used for a wide range of elements; they may be obtained commercially, but are relatively easy to make (see pp. 14-18). Several manufacturers[11] produce lamps covering about thirty different elements, although not all are suitable for atomic-absorption spectrophotometry.

The lamp consists of a hollow cylinder made from material containing the element to be determined, enclosed in a low pressure rare-gas atmosphere, and is energized by a potential of about 400 V with a current of up to 100 m A. The spectrum of the glow discharge is characteristic of the cathode material and the carrier gas. If helium is the carrier gas, the characteristic spectrum of the cathode material is largely due to ions (spark spectrum), since excitation is due to collisions of the second kind, the ionization potential of helium (19·7 eV) being above that of most other elements. Arc lines (lines due to the atom) are more prevalent when argon is used as the carrier gas because of its lower ionization potential. This is preferred, because the resonance lines of the cathode material are thereby enhanced. Three different methods of energizing the hollow-cathode lamp have been used; namely, stabilized voltage d.c.,[8] stabilized current d.c.[12, 13] and stabilized voltage a.c. David,[14] using the a.c. supply, maintained that the difficulty arising from flame emission (page 9) may be overcome by making measurements with a detector and a 50 c/s tuned amplifier, thus eliminating any d.c. signal due to emission from the flame.

Russell and Walsh[15] suggest that scattered radiation, obtained from hollow-cathode lamps emitted at right angles to the axis of the hollow cathode, may be used to advantage, because it almost entirely consists of the resonance radiation due to the cathode material. Although the intensity of scattered radiation is low, this is offset because a monochromator is not required for wavelength selection.

Details of a simple means of making hollow-cathode lamps will now be described; for fuller details of the principles and methods of operation of sharp line sources, reference should be made to Tolansky's *High Resolution Spectroscopy*.[16]

3.2 HOLLOW-CATHODE LAMPS

Hollow-cathode lamps have been used in spectroscopic experiments for at least forty years, either as a means for exciting the sample for spectrographic analysis, or, more frequently, the production of very sharp spectrum lines in the investigation of hyperfine structure of spectrum lines. Tolansky[16] has described the historical use of these lamps and also their construction for use in hyperfine structure experiments. Such lamps often have specially cooled cathodes and are invariably operated in conjunction with a vacuum circulating system in which any impurities present in the supporting gas, due to outgassing, are continuously removed. More recently, Dieke and Crosswhite[17] have used activated uranium as an efficient getter in the production of sealed-off iron hollow-cathode lamps; details of the production of these lamps, and their properties, are given, and it is reported that they have a long life.[18] Russell, Shelton and Walsh[8] have also made sealed-off hollow-cathode lamps with a variety of cathode materials, using tantalum or zirconium as the getter. Subsequently, Jones and Walsh[19] described the construction and characteristics of sealed-off hollow-cathode lamps suitable as spectroscopic light sources. They indicate that difficulties generally associated with the production of sealed-off lamps appear to have been unduly exaggerated, and that suitable lamps for atomic-absorption spectrophotometry can be made easily for a variety of elements in which the particular element constitutes the cathode material. These views are in accord with experience in the authors' laboratory.

Hilger and Watts Ltd. independently developed sealed-off hollow-cathode lamps[20] and have been producing them for several years. The modified design detailed in Section 3.3 embodies the basic features of the Hilger and Watts lamp.

3.3 DESIGN AND PRODUCTION OF LAMP

The basic requirements are that a hollow cylindrical-cathode (dimensions about $\frac{1}{2}$ in. i.d. $\times \frac{3}{4}$ in. long) is mounted in a vacuum tight vessel, of at least 150 ml capacity, containing a rare gas (usually argon) at a pressure of about 2 mm Hg, with a simple anode connection and a suitable window for observing the cathode glow. The form of lamp used by the authors is shown in Fig. 2.

A 250 ml thick walled round bottom flask, selected for its uniformity, has two side arms fitted with B10 and B24 conical sockets and a neck constricted to take a 20 mm diameter quartz window, cemented on with black wax. An anode, consisting of a 1 mm diameter tungsten rod, is sealed into a B10 cone and a similar tungsten cathode connection is fitted into the B24 cone. The cathode is crimped on to the tungsten connection and supported by a glass tube.

The form of the cathode varies from element to element but where possible it is machined from a solid piece of metal in order to reduce small crevices which may be difficult to outgas.

Some metals, e.g. cadmium, with comparatively low melting points may not have the required rigidity for a solid cathode and are supported by casting a small solid slug in a machined

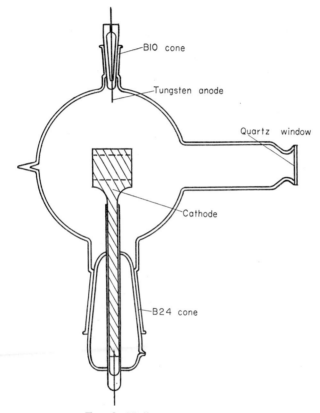

FIG. 2. Hollow-cathode lamp.

aluminium cathode which is subsequently drilled to give the hollow cathode.

If expensive metals are to be used, the metal foil may be placed in the cylindrical cavity of an aluminium cathode.

Before the constituent parts are fitted together, they are thoroughly cleaned by pickling in an appropriate acid, after which they are washed in water, then degreased in acetone; the tungsten connections are cleaned in an aqueous solution of sodium nitrite. After being cleaned in this way, the lamp is assembled, the cone joints are sealed with black wax and the lamp is attached to a vacuum system, then rapidly evacuated.

A typical vacuum system used is shown in the schematic diagram (Fig. 3). It consists of a conventional rotary backing pump (P1), a mercury diffusion-pump (P2), a ballast volume (V1) of 1 litre capacity, a cold trap (F) and an injection volume (V2) of 100 ml capacity. T1–T6 are high vacuum taps and M is a sealed mercury manometer. High-purity argon from a cylinder is passed through two purifying traps (A and B) containing Anhydrone (anhydrous magnesium perchlorate) and soda asbestos. A fine capillary (C) (about 0.1 mm diameter $\times 2$ cm) is used to control the flow of argon into the injection volume (V2). The ratio of total volume (comprising that of V1+V2+lamp +connection tubing) to injection volume (V2) is determined by a preliminary pressure calibration. In the apparatus shown in Fig. 3 this ratio is 22 : 1. Thus, by having a pressure of argon of about 2–4 cm Hg in V2, and expanding the gas into the whole apparatus, controlled pressures in the range 1–2 mm Hg argon, can easily be obtained. A McLeod gauge is used for measuring residual pressure in the vacuum system, and the hollow-cathode lamp is sealed to the outlet side of the cold trap. Production of the lamp is completed as follows:

The entire vacuum system is evacuated to a pressure of less than 10^{-5} mm Hg: the lamp is then tested for leaks. After the lamp has been maintained at a low pressure for half an hour, argon is passed into the injection volume and subsequently expanded into the whole apparatus, so that a final pressure of 1·5–2 mm Hg is obtained. The lamp is energized by a simple 600 V 200 mA (max) d.c. power supply and a glow discharge is produced. After running for 5–10 min, to heat up the cathode, the lamp is rapidly evacuated by first closing tap T4 and pumping down the remainder of the apparatus, then subsequently opening T4. This process of filling, running the discharge and rapid pumping is repeated several times in order

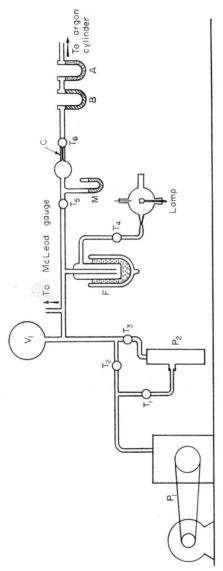

Fig. 3. Schematic diagram of apparatus used for the production of hollow-cathode lamps.

to outgas the lamp. The cathode glow will be seen to change as the argon pressure is reduced, and the pressure at which there is a maximum intensity of glow from inside the cathode is chosen for the final filling: tap T4 is then closed and the lamp current is increased until cathodic sputtering occurs (usually 50–100 mA). In the production of hollow-cathode lamps containing low melting point metals, it may be necessary to use a lower maximum current to avoid melting, e.g. cadmium, for which 20 mA should not be exceeded. The lamp is left running for several hours, to ensure that no leaks occur, and finally it is sealed off from the vacuum system. Figure 4 shows the constituent parts of a hollow-cathode lamp, and also the assembled unit.

3.4 MEANS OF VAPORIZING SAMPLE

Most workers have used conventional atomizers and burners for producing atomic vapour of the sample solution. Requirements for the atomizer are the same as for emission flame-photometry, viz. incorporating a system for ensuring a reproducible supply of consistently fine droplets of solution. The most effective atomizer will produce the largest number of droplets vaporized into the flame per unit time.

In emission flame-photometry, different instrumental arrangements are likely, and this makes a comparison of atomizer efficiencies difficult; the measurement of emission intensity also necessarily involves other equipment of uncertain efficiency, e.g. light-gathering power, scattered light intensities in monochromators, and gain in output amplifier circuits. It has been suggested[12] that absorption measurements, where ratios of intensities are used, are more suitable for establishing relative atomizer efficiencies, because other experimental factors are eliminated. This reasoning will only be valid if the lamp and flame conditions are identical, because these factors can also affect the measured absorption. A discussion of factors influencing atomizer efficiency and their

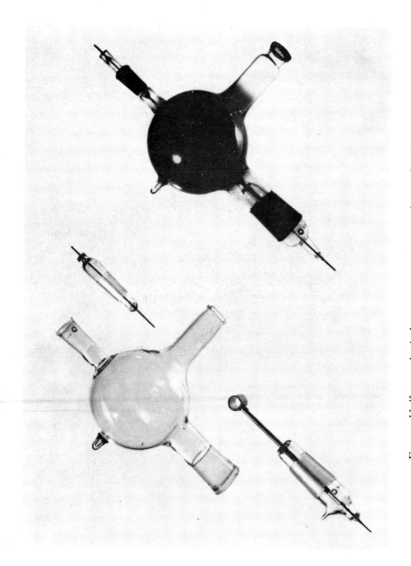

Fig. 4. Hollow-cathode lamp—components and completed unit.

effects on atomic-absorption measurements is given later (Section 4.1.1, page 25).

As indicated previously, flame temperature does not influence absorption characteristics significantly, provided a sufficiently high temperature is available to produce an atomic vapour of the element being determined. There are several elements, however, that do not produce significant amounts of atomic vapour in flames produced from conventional fuels. For this reason, atomic-absorption measurements have not been successful in the determination of elements such as aluminium, titanium, silicon. Magnesium, for which high sensitivity is obtained,[8, 12] is only partially vaporized at normal flame temperatures, and it has been calculated[21] that only about 1·5 % of the total magnesium is dissociated into atoms at a temperature of 2410°K in an air/acetylene flame. If much higher temperature flames could be used, it is reasonable to expect that increased sensitivity would be obtained, at least for some elements. The use of an oxy-cyanogen flame,[22] for which temperatures of about 4600°K are claimed, or a plasma-arc discharge,[23] in which temperatures exceeding 15,000°K have been achieved, would certainly increase the sensitivity for some elements and enable atomic vapour of others, e.g. aluminium, titanium, to be obtained. One factor which should not be overlooked, however, is that at these very high temperatures the average energy of the flame would be sufficient to ionize, or otherwise excite, a large proportion of atoms present and this would obviously deplete the number of atoms in the unexcited ground state; a compromise would have to be sought between the higher concentration of atomic vapour and the reduced proportion of atoms in the ground state.

For various reasons, which will now be discussed, the shape of the flame is important. The absorption (optical density) is defined by the relation $\log_{10}(I_0/I) = K_{max}l$ where K_{max} is the absorption coefficient at the centre of the line and l the length of the absorbing path. K_{max} is proportional to the concentration or number of atoms/cm^3. The measured optical density will, therefore, be proportional to both the length of the flame and the concentration of the atoms present. With constant atomizer conditions the concentration of atoms is inversely proportional to the horizontal cross-sectional area of the flame; an increase in length of the burner would, therefore, decrease the atomic concentration proportionally. Thus, the measured optical density would remain constant. An increase in optical density can be achieved, however, by reducing the *width* of the flame, either with or without an increase in flame length, so that either an increased atomic concentration or an increased length of flame, is obtained without a corresponding decrease in the other factor.

Although an atomizer-flame system is the only vapour source at present used in practical applications of atomic absorption spectrophotometry, other sources may be developed in the future. Gatehouse and Walsh[24] have described a method in which sputtering from a metal surface in the presence of argon, at a pressure of 1 mm (Hg), enabled 1 ppm of silver to be determined in a copper alloy. They suggest that this method has potential applications in the determination of elements such as aluminium and boron, which do not give rise to atoms under normal flame conditions. The obvious experimental difficulties and the need for analysed standards are, at present, two serious limitations to application of the method.

Various optical arrangements may be used for passing light through atomic vapour. Satisfactory results can be obtained by simply placing the flame between the sharp-line source and the wavelength selector, provided a stable light source is used and there is negligible emission from the flame at the resonance wavelength. It is possible to eliminate, almost completely, any effect due to flame emission by placing the flame between two lenses, so that a parallel beam of radiation from the sharp-line source passes through the flame and is subsequently focused on to the wavelength selector. In this way light emitted from the flame will be defocused at the wavelength selector and hence will have a minimal effect.[13] This has proved satisfactory for many elements, except where the flame intensity is much greater than the sharp-line source intensity; e.g. with high concentrations of sodium using a considerably under-run sodium vapour lamp. Under these conditions, curvature of the calibration graph towards the concentration axis occurs (page 7), limiting the useful range of the determination to low concentrations. Using a.c. operated hollow-cathode lamps, the d.c. signal, due to the flame emission, can be eliminated by incorporating an a.c. amplifier tuned to the lamp supply frequency in the measuring circuit.[14] A double beam system can be used[8] in which the light beam is split and chopped at different frequencies, one beam by-passing the flame and recombining with the second beam before entering the monochromator. From a ratio of the outputs from two amplifiers tuned to the two frequencies, effects due to flame emission and lamp fluctuations can be eliminated.

Increased sensitivity can be obtained by passing the light beam through the atomic vapour several times. Russell, Shelton and Walsh,[8] have increased the sensitivity of the detection of iron six-fold, by traversing the flame twelve times; a principle first devised by White.[25] With this type of system, however, a fairly broad flame is necessary and the advantages of a narrow flame are lost.

When light is directed through a flame it is essential to avoid any by-passing, which would produce a reduction in the measured absorption and result in a curved calibration graph. It has been demonstrated[26] that the position within the flame is also important and diaphragms restricting the area of flame used can increase absorption at a given concentration (see calcium, page 83).

3.5 WAVELENGTH SELECTOR

In the simplest form, a coloured glass or gelatine filter is sufficient, but in many instances a good ultraviolet monochromator is necessary for selecting the required wavelength. A basic requirement for a wavelength selector is its ability to separate one line (the absorption line) from all other lines emitted by the sharp-line source. If any background radiation is emitted by the sharp-line source, a curved calibration graph will again be produced, but the curvature may be minimized by using a narrow band-pass monochromator, which reduces the proportion of unabsorbed light.

With sharp-line sources which emit the element resonance line in the visible region with high intensity and practically no other radiation, e.g. a sodium vapour lamp, selection of the resonance line can be made with simple coloured glass filters. In other cases, where the resonance line is in the visible, or near ultraviolet region, interference filters may be used as selectors provided no lines, other than the resonance line, are within the band-width of the filter. Interference filters are not suitable if the sharp-line source emits background radiation, because this would be transmitted over the whole band-width of the filter. Background radiation is not absorbed in the flame and would, therefore, reduce the measured absorption and produce curved calibration graphs. The commonest, and most versatile, wavelength selection system, is a monochromator capable of variable wavelength selection. Modified ultraviolet spectrophotometers,[8, 13] and quartz prism spectrographs[12, 14] have been used successfully in atomic absorption work, for this purpose. If the monochromator is unable to resolve the line being measured from other radiations from the lamp, i.e. other lines or background radiation, the measured absorption will be reduced and again result in a curved calibration graph. This was confirmed by Allan[27] who demonstrated that interference due to unresolved lines and background radiation caused considerable reduction in sensitivity in the determination of iron and manganese respectively.

3.6 INTENSITY MEASUREMENT AND RECORDING

Standard methods for measuring light intensity are used and little comment is necessary. For instruments using either interference or coloured filters for wavelength selection, it is possible to use a simple barrier-layer photocell and galvanometer for intensity measurement, but in most other instances, photomultiplier detectors are the most useful. They are very sensitive light-detectors, sensitivity being controlled by the voltage applied to the secondary electrodes (dynodes), and cover a wide useful wavelength range. In the authors' laboratory a standard RCA IP.28 tube has been used for measurements in the range 2100 to 6800 Å, although at the high wavelengths, sensitivity of response was much reduced. The high sensitivity of photomultipliers allows narrow slit widths and low hollow-cathode lamp currents to be used; factors which influence the sensitivity of the method.

Various methods are used for measuring the photomultiplier output current; a simple galvanometer system can be used,[12] provided very low currents are not being measured. Alternatively, an amplifying circuit may be used.[14] With the chopped d.c. signal obtained from double-beam systems used by Walsh,[8] the two signals of different frequencies are amplified and ratioed, the final result being indicated on a chart record. It has been shown in the authors' laboratory that an integrating system[28] can be used to advantage when the light intensity to be measured has small short-term fluctuations.[29] The same circuit can be used to give an instantaneous intensity reading, all measurements being made on a null-balance principle. The full diagrams of a simple a.c. amplifier circuit, together with details of the sharp-line source a.c. power supply are given by Box and Walsh.[30]

Most of the methods described give a measure of intensity, or percentage transmission, whereas optical density is the characteristic to be determined. A logarithmic scale, or chart can be used, or alternatively the optical density can be obtained by simple calculation. It is stressed, however, that, if a linear intensity scale is used, any measuring or reading errors will have varying effects, depending on the determined optical density value. Optical densities in the range of about 0.15–1.0 (70–10% transmission) are, therefore, preferred, because measurements outside this range are more liable to excessive measurement errors. These comments apply to intensity measurements, but in determinations where a curved calibration graph is used, it may be advisable to lower the upper (1.0) optical density limit.

CHAPTER 4

GENERAL CONSIDERATIONS

4.1 COMPARISON WITH FLAME PHOTOMETRY

IN the paper[3] in which the application of atomic absorption to chemical analysis was first described, Walsh states (p. 115) that "one of the main attractions of this absorption method is that, theoretically, it is expected to be much less susceptible to inter-element effects"; a statement that justifies a comparison of the principles involved in atomic absorption and emission flame-photometry. These two procedures, as generally applied, will differ only in the method of measuring atomic-vapour concentrations in a flame and hence Walsh's statement can only apply to those inter-element effects which have a direct bearing on this measurement.

Processes involved in both emission flame-photometry and atomic absorption are discussed in the following three sub-sections.

4.1.1 *Atomization of a liquid*

The term "atomization" here means the production of a mist in a stream of air, or other supporting gas of the flame. Some workers[31] have used a combined atomizer-burner of the Beckman type, but the majority prefer a separate atomizing system, because this allows greater flexibility in flame character-istics, e.g. shape and gas composition. Where a separate atomizer and burner are used, it is customary to interpose an expansion chamber, thus permitting only the smallest droplets to pass into the gas stream of the burner. In practice, it is found that a maximnm of about 10% of the spray from the atomizer is in the form of small droplets which pass through the expansion chamber, and Menzies[32] has suggested that these droplets are, in fact, Plateaus' spherules (small secondary droplets which often form behind larger main drops).

Both the rate of atomization and ratio of liquid in the drops and droplets are dependent, not only on characteristics of the atomizer, but also on physical properties of the solution, e.g. its viscosity and surface tension. Thus a change in the concentration of the solute, or the use of an alternative solvent or reagent, could influence the physical properties of a solution sufficiently to cause a change in the rate of atomization. Effects due to these variables are discussed later (cf. zinc, page 50, and lead page 60) and further experiments to demonstrate the effect of organic reagents will now be described and discussed.

Independent solutions containing iron, magnesium, zinc and lead in a water/iso-propyl alcohol (3 + 2) mixture were prepared. Each solution was separately sprayed into the flame and absorptions were recorded. The amount of fine spray reaching the flame was measured by passing the spray emerging from the expansion chamber into a long spiral glass tube, partially immersed in a freezing mixture of solid carbon dioxide and acetone; the amount of spray collected in a given time was subsequently weighed. Similar measurements were made on aqueous solutions containing the same amounts of the various metals and the two sets of values were compared. It was found that absorption increased in the presence of iso-propyl alcohol, due almost entirely to an increase in the rate of production of fine spray (Table 3). (See also Copper, page 93.)

These comparisons were made using an air/coal-gas flame and will not necessarily be the same in other flames, or in the presence of other organic media.

The increased absorption indicated in Table 3 appears to be of value for improving the sensitivity of the method in the determination of low concentrations, but in practice the advantage of this greater absorption would be offset if addition of the organic reagent necessarily increased dilution of the sample solution. If the sample can be retained in solution in a wholly organic medium, then full advantage can be taken of the increased sensitivity. One method by which this can be achieved is by using organic complexing agents and extracting the resultant complex into an organic solvent. In this way greater sensitivity will result, not only from the increased concentration of the extracted element, but also from the enhancement

TABLE 3.

RATIO OF ABSORPTIONS AND SPRAY
RATES OF WATER/ISO-PROPYL ALCOHOL
(3 + 2) AND AQUEOUS SOLUTIONS

Element	Ratio of absorptions	Ratio of spray rates
Iron	2·4	
Magnesium	2·0	1·8
Zinc	1·8	
Lead	1·9	

obtained in the presence of the organic solvent. Allan[33] describes experiments designed to establish the cause of enhancement of absorption due to the presence of various organic reagents and reaches the same general conclusions, but Lockyer, Scott and Slade,[34] using ostensibly the same equipment, report much greater enhancement for iron. It has also been claimed that greater enhancement can be obtained using different atomizer and burner arrangements.[35] The claim that some solvents enhance sensitivity by a factor of up to 40 is not apparently connected with atomizer efficiency and this is discussed later (page 31).

4.1.2 *Flame effects on suspension of fine droplets introduced into the supporting gas-stream*

The behaviour of an aqueous solution can be considered as proceeding in several stages.

Droplets of the solvent evaporate and a solid particle remains. Menzies[6] has suggested the name "clot" for such particles but later,[32] he proposed the name "clotlet" as being more appropriate. Subsequent stages in this process are calcination, when various changes may take place, e.g. the elimination of a more volatile constituent, chemical interaction between the various inorganic substances present, including the flame gases, melting of the product and finally, partial or complete volatilization of the residue. For these consecutive stages to be efficient, all must proceed very rapidly. It is estimated that less than 10 msec is taken for a particle to pass through 1 cm of a typical flame so that, for the efficient production of atomic vapour, conversion of droplets into vapour must take only a small fraction of this time.

Baker[36] has discussed interferences which may occur due to incomplete volatilization of clotlets, with particular reference to the suppression effect of phosphate on calcium absorption; the most important facts may be summarized as follows:

(a) Behaviour is similar in both emission and absorption and is, therefore, dependent only on the production of atoms in the flame.

(b) As the concentration of phosphate is increased, the apparent concentration of calcium atoms decreases up to a point where calcium and phosphate are present in about equimolar proportions.

(c) There is no suppression when calcium and phosphate are independently introduced into the flame from separate atomizers.

Suppression can be reduced or eliminated in several ways, including:

(i) Dilution of the solution.

(ii) Use of more efficient atomizers to produce smaller droplets.

(iii) Using the tip of a long non-turbulent flame in the measurement.

(iv) Addition of various reagents, including magnesium sulphate, sodium ethylenediaminetetracetate (EDTA) and the chlorides of strontium, lanthanum, iron, yttrium, scandium and the rare earths.

Baker[36] goes on further to suggest possible mechanisms for these interferences and means for overcoming them. He suggests that evaporation of the droplets, and later dissociation of the vapour, takes place rapidly, and in a similar manner for all but the most refractory materials. However, the intermediate process of vaporization of the dry residue must be considered in relation to certain physical parameters. It is the *rate* of vaporization, compared with the transit time of the particle through the flame, which determines the extent to which the residue is vaporized, and the most important variables controlling this are probably boiling-point, vapour pressure and particle size.

In the case of a clotlet, with a boiling-point below the temperature of the flame, e.g. alkali chlorides, the vapour pressure will be at least one atmosphere and the rate of vaporization almost instantaneous, compared with its transit time through the flame. If, however, the clotlet boils above the temperature of the flame, the vapour pressure may be only a small fraction of an atmosphere and the rate of vaporization such that only a small proportion of it will have vaporized before it is discharged from the high temperature region of the flame. Under these circumstances, the particle size and vapour pressure will be important parameters.

In the first two methods for overcoming interference, viz. dilution of the solution and the use of a more efficient atomizer, resulting clotlets of calcium phosphate are much smaller and hence have a larger surface area per unit volume. There is, therefore, a greater rate of vaporization and hence more calcium atoms are produced. Using the tip of a long low-turbulent flame, the transit time for an individual clotlet is increased, with a corresponding increase in the number of atoms formed from the clotlet.

Dry clotlets formed from various reagents, added to overcome phosphate interference, may vaporize and react in several ways. For example:

(a) Chemical reaction with calcium phosphate may take place and give rise to a more volatile calcium salt.

(b) A homogeneous melt may form and vaporizes as a single substance.

(c) A melt may form from which the added constituent evaporates selectively at first, followed by simultaneous vaporization of the two independent constituents.

(d) The added constituent may vaporize completely before the calcium phosphate.

Even in this last, least favourable case, it is unlikely that the added constituent would vaporize leaving a compact clotlet of calcium phosphate identical with that which would have existed in the absence of an added constituent. Under these conditions it is much more likely that the calcium phosphate will be dispersed either as ultra-fine particles or as particles with a "honeycomb" or "sponge" structure. In both cases the surface area per unit volume would be extremely large and hence result in a much higher rate of vaporization.

Baker[36] has carried out experiments on the vaporization of clotlets to test the validity of his theories. In particular he has examined the so-called complexing effect of the sodium salt of EDTA[37] because he considers it invalid to suggest that the property of complex formation could affect the rate of vaporization of a clotlet. He made a comparison of the behaviour of the sodium and ammonium salts of EDTA and found that the sodium salt was more effective as a suppressing agent, particularly at low concentrations. The next logical step was to examine the effect of other sodium salts and it was found that sodium chloride was even more effective as an interference suppressor, thus the complexing action of EDTA probably had little effect on the rate of vaporization of the clotlet, an observation that was substantiated by using another water soluble organic compound (sucrose) which he found to be very effective. It is apparent from the results of these few tests, and the behaviour of a range of other interference suppressors investigated by other workers, that a complete systematic study of these effects is essential before the mechanism of interference and suppression can be fully understood.

The rate of vaporization of clotlets is important, not only from an interference point-of-view, but also as a means for increasing sensitivity. Robinson[35] has investigated the effects of organic solvents on both the emission and absorption characteristics of nickel in an oxy-cyanogen flame, and obtained relative emission intensity and absorption measurements for various organic media and water. Because there is an enhancement in both absorption and emission, this cannot simply be attributed to an increase in flame temperature and Robinson suggests that enhancements are due to the presence of a greater number of atoms in the flame, produced by the more efficient volatilization of droplets. The production of atoms from an aqueous droplet is almost entirely endothermic whereas, after vaporization of organic reagents, the preliminary dissociation of organo-metallic compounds, is usually exothermic and hence may proceed at a greater rate under the same conditions. A thirty-six-fold increase in absorption signal was reported by Robinson in atomic-absorption experiments in which acetone replaced water; this was obtained with an oxy-cyanogen flame, probably (unstated) with direct atomization into the flame, but this enhancement may not be achieved with more conventional flames incorporating indirect atomization. If the explanation proposed by Robinson is correct, enhancement of emission and absorption signals should be similar, but his results on a range of organic solvents show the ratio of enhancement of absorption to emission varying between 1·4 and 8, instead of unity. These discrepancies may be due to self-absorption of the emission signal or variations in the flame characteristics which affect absorption and emission differently, although Robinson offers no explanation.

4.1.3 *Flame effects on atomic-vapour concentration*

The final stage in the determination of any element by either procedure is measurement of the emitted or absorbed signal. It has already been shown (page 4) that the number of excited atoms is critically dependent on temperature, whereas the number of atoms remaining in the ground state is almost unaffected. It is obvious that if sufficient energy is available in the flame, a proportion of the atoms present will be ionized, thus removing atoms from the unionized ground state, or low excited state. In this way both absorption and emission will be reduced due to the lower number of atoms in suitable states. This is particularly noticeable with the alkali metals which have low ionization potentials, and hence are significantly ionized in very hot flames. This will make the number of atoms in the ground state, and hence the absorption, dependent on temperature.

The effect of additional elements on ionization is important. For example, Baker,[36] using any oxy-propane flame for determining potassium by emission, has shown that the presence of 100 ppm of lithium increased the apparent potassium concentration by 55 %; the same amount of caesium produced an enhancement of 200 %.

When these experiments were repeated, and absorption measurements made using a similar oxy-propane flame, enhancements were again obtained, but only to about half the extent of those obtained in emission.

Figure 5 shows a comparison between effects on emission and absorption, of potassium, when other alkali metals are present.

These interferences are thought to be due to the high absorption of energy involved in ionizing the added alkali with a consequent increase in the number of unionized potassium atoms capable to taking part in normal emission or absorption, depending upon their excitation state. Baker suggests that emission and absorption enhancements are different, because of the slightly different gas-flow rates used for the burner in the absorption measurements or, alternatively, the differing extent of enhancement on the population of atoms in the ground state or excited states. This suggested mechanism of alkali inter-

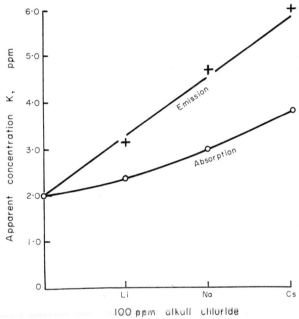

FIG. 5. Effect of other alkalies on potassium determination.
(Reproduced by kind permission of Dr. C. A. Baker)

ferences was substantiated when he made similar tests with a cooler air/coal-gas Meker flame and observed no enhancement either in emission or absorption. Foster and Hume[38] have shown that at temperatures of 2000–3000°C, alkali metal compounds are dissociated into the atomic state; some atoms are also ionized. For example, at 2000°C potassium is stated to be more than 80% ionized, thus leaving less than 20% of the atoms available from transitions corresponding to the resonance line at 7665 Å. In the cooler flame of an air/coal-gas burner, only a few per cent of potassium atoms are ionized and a change in the population of the unionized states is insignificant when the energy of the flame is reduced by the introduction of other alkali metals.

4.1.4 *Measurement of emission or absorption*

In the discussion so far, factors which have been considered, influence both absorption and emission to the same extent. With the measurement of either absorption or emission, however, there are several significant differences. It is frequently found in emission flame-photometry that the line of analytical interest is accompanied by lines due to other constituents of the sample, and interferences may occur due to inefficiency in the resolution of lines by the monochromator when an excess of another element is present. For example, in the determination of magnesium in the presence of excess sodium, the lines Mg $2852 \cdot 13$ Å and Na $2852 \cdot 83$ Å are not easily resolved. Such interferences are not likely to occur in absorption, because the effective band-width of the monochromator is the width of the lamp emission line, i.e. of the order of $0 \cdot 01$ Å.

A similar form of optical interference which is frequently encountered in flame photometry, particularly in trace analysis, is background emission. This may be due to continuous radiation from the flame or, more likely, from emission-band spectra from other constituents of the sample. By making measurements of the background immediately adjacent to the line, it is possible to make suitable corrections. If background and line intensities are measured by integration over the same period of time, it is possible to make accurate corrections, thereby enabling low line intensities to be measured in the presence of high background. In this way accurate measurements of line intensities with line to background intensity ratios as small as $1:400$ have been reported.[39]

It is unlikely that the transitions which cause background emission are also capable of producing absorption under flame conditions and, therefore, there will be no counterpart to background emission interference in absorption measurements.

In addition, the effective band-width of the monochromator is of the order 0.01 Å in absorption measurements, compared with, say, 5 Å in emission measurements and this would again result in a considerable decrease in the effect of any possible background absorption.

A comparison of the causes of interference in both emission and absorption may be summarized as follows:

(a) Variation of atomizer efficiency using solutions with different physical characteristics.

(b) Different rates of vaporization in the flame due to variation in the composition of the solutions.

(c) Changes in flame characteristics with subsequent variations in the proportion of atoms in the ground, excited or ionized states.

(d) Radiation reaching the detector from sources other than the element being determined.

Atomic absorption is not affected by radiation interference, particularly if a modulated light source is used. Variations in the ground and excited state populations caused by temperature variations will not affect absorption measurements, provided the number of ionized atoms is small. Interferences due to a variation in the proportion of ionized atoms, differing rates of vaporization and atomizer efficiency, will affect both absorption and emission similarly. Thus the original statement of Walsh concerning freedom from interferences, needs considerable qualification when practical aspects of atomic-absorption spectrophotometry are being considered.

A further difference exists between the methods of making measurements of flame emission and absorption. Near the limit of detection, measurement of an emission signal is controlled by the noise in the measuring amplifier circuit, because the maximum available gain is used. In absorption, however, at the limit of detection, it is necessary to measure a small difference between two appreciable signals. Thus, for the highest sensitivity a measuring circuit of high gain and low noise is required for emission, whereas high stabillity is the essential factor in low absorption measurements.

Compared with emission, absorption procedures lack a simple rapid means of varying sensitivity, when dealing with solutions containing widely varying amounts of the elements being determined because, whereas sensitivity of emission measurements can be varied, merely by altering the gain of the measuring circuit, the sensitivity of absorption measurements is determined almost entirely by flame characteristics, e.g. flame length.

It has already been stated that for accurate measurements, absorption should be restricted to optical densities in the range $0.15–1.0$ ($70–10\%$ transmission) although for determinations where the highest accuracies are not required, this range may be extended, particularly in the low absorption region. Thus it is possible to determine an element with a high degree of accuracy over a range of up to twenty fold, but at concentrations in excess of this, further dilution of the sample is advisable.

Clinton[40] has described the construction of a burner for an oxy-acetylene flame which may be used with a variable absorption-path length to produce a reduction in sensitivity by a factor of twelve. This is achieved by rotating the burner about an axis at right angles to the optical axis of the monochromator. By use of a flame of variable path-length, or a double-beam system to enable accurate measurement of low absorption to be made, it should be possible to make accurate determinations over at least a thousand-fold range.

4.2 COMPARISON WITH OTHER METHODS

When methods other than flame photometry are compared with atomic absorption, it is only possible to make general comparisons. If sample pre-treatment, method of measurement, standardization, reproducibility and accuracy are considered, a reasonably clear indication of the relative value of each method can be obtained.

Emission spectrographic methods for examining solid samples, usually entail a minimum of sample pretreatment, for example, with metallurgical samples either filing or machining is all that is required. Excitation is usually straightforward, but measurements of spectrum intensities may be long and tedious if microphotometric methods are used. With emission spectrographic methods several elements can be determined simultaneously and a permanent record is available. Where increased speed and accuracy of intensity measurement are desirable, photoelectric recording is introduced, but versatility is sacrificed. In this branch of analysis, chemically analysed standard samples, in the same physical form as the test samples, are essential for calibration purposes and it is equally important that the composition of standard and test samples should be very similar, to minimize any inter-element effects. Reproducibilities as good as 1·5% (expressed as a coefficient of variation) have been achieved photographically[41] and even better results, of the order of 0·5%, can be obtained consistently under routine conditions with photoelectric spectrometers.[1] Accuracies are dependent on a combination of standardization and reproducibility and, when adequate standards are available, accuracies are of the same order as the values quoted for reproducibility.

The problem of obtaining chemically analysed standards in the same physical form as the samples to be examined may be avoided by using a solution method. The reproducibility of solution methods are, however, usually, not as good as the best methods in which solid standards are used, although, under routine conditions in the authors' laboratory, a reproducibility of about 2% is achieved regularly in the determination of about 3% zirconium in hafnium, using a "polythene cup" solution method. Even with solution methods it is essential to provide standards of similar composition to the samples, because inter-element effects, though smaller than with solid samples, are not eliminated.

In the determination of most metallic elements, sensitivities obtained by direct spectrographic or spectrometric methods are greater than can be achieved at present by any method based on atomic absorption, this is due mainly to the dilution effect brought about by dissolving the sample. In the authors' laboratory, however, atomic-absorption methods have been used for standardizing spectrographic and spectrometric samples.

A wide range of both metals and non-metals can be determined by methods based on the use of X-ray fluorescence, with the exception of elements with atomic numbers lower than 12, using a vacuum-path instrument, and 22 where the instrument incorporates an air-path. In X-ray fluorescence analysis, sample pretreatment is similar to that required in optical emission methods and, because of inter-element effects, which can be severe, standardization problems in both methods are similar. The fluorescent X-ray beam is usually measured by a photon counter and the reproducibility of these measurements is controlled by the total number of pulses counted. In the determination of major constituents, reproducibilities and accuracies of the same order can be achieved, provided adequate standardization is made.

Because it is possible, using either emission spectrometric (direct reading) or X-ray flourescence methods, to determine several elements concurrently, with speed and accuracy, these procedures are widely applied in the routine examination of inorganic samples where variations in composition are small, particularly if such samples can readily be made available in a standardized form. Atomic-absorption methods, therefore, in their present state of development, are not serious rivals to these methods, although it is possible that developments of a sputtering technique[24] may result in some elements being analysed with improved efficiency by atomic absorption. In particular, the high capital costs of present-day instruments, for rapid routine analyses, makes the use of comparatively cheap apparatus an attractive proposition. A complete atomic absorption apparatus can be purchased for about £1000, compared with, say over £12,000 for automatic X-ray fluorescence equipment.

In colorimetric analysis, reagents are available for producing coloured complexes for more than half of the elements in the periodic table, but few are specific and a chemical separation is frequently necessary in order to eliminate ions present in the sample solution which would otherwise interfere in the determination. A reliable calibration graph must be prepared but, provided the characteristic colour is stable, this usually does not present a problem, and an overall precision for the determination, of about 2%, can reasonably be expected. Using differential colorimetric procedures, it is possible to increase this precision considerably; for example, when applied to the determination of copper, values of between 99·80 and 100·15% were obtained[42] but, because of the elaborate precautions and very careful attention to detail which are necessary, procedures of this type are restricted in their application.

Where simple and sensitive colorimetric methods are applicable, there may be little advantage to be gained by using an atomic-absorption procedure, but where interferences occur which necessitate a preliminary treatment of the sample solution, the rapidity and simplicity of the atomic-absorption method makes it particularly attractive.

In many respects polarographic and colorimetric procedures have similar limitations, so that a comparison between colorimetric and polarographic procedures, on the one hand, and atomic absorption procedures, on the other, are the same.

Polarographic waves can be obtained for more than half of the common elements, but separations from the matrix elements are frequently necessary, unless an expensive polarograph with high resolution is used. Precisions of about 2% can be readily achieved with most polarographs.

Comparisons, between conventional analytical procedures, and procedures based on atomic absorption, could be extended, but comments would be similar to those already made. What will be appreciated, however, is that the simplicity of the majority of atomic-absorption procedures compares very favourably with alternative chemical or instrumental methods. Sensitivities of atomic-absorption procedures vary between elements but some elements, e.g. zinc, cadmium, magnesium, are probably more easily determined by atomic absorption than by any other simple procedure. The precision of a determination compares favourably with many other instrumental methods (about 2%) and, because of its high specificity, accuracies are also high.

In any modern laboratory in which inorganic analyses are undertaken, an atomic-absorption spectrophotometer will profitably take a place with other physico-chemical instruments which are likely to be much more expensive.

CHAPTER 5

DETAILED CONSIDERATIONS

APART from reference to use of atomic absorption in a study of stellar atmospheres,[43] the determination of mercury vapour in the atmosphere[44] appears to be the only analytical application of the principle, prior to publication of Walsh's paper[3] in 1955. Since 1955, information regarding the determination of at least twenty-three metallic elements has been published, including detailed applications for determining sodium, potassium, magnesium, calcium, zinc, lead, iron, manganese and some of the noble metals. These determinations have been made in a wide variety of materials, ranging from agricultural materials (plant ash and soil extracts) and biological materials (blood serum) to metallurgical samples of complex composition. Advantages gained by the introduction of atomic-absorption spectrophotometry are varied, in some instances time-consuming chemical procedures have been replaced by simpler and more rapid procedures, in others, e.g. flame photometry has been replaced by a technique which is less prone to inter-element interferences. At first sight it may appear possible to extend the list of elements capable of being determined by atomic-absorption spectrophotometry to cover the whole of the periodic table but, at present, using an atomizer and flame as a means for producing atomic vapour, two main limitations are known. Firstly, some elements are not dissociated into atomic form in the flame, because of the formation of refractory compounds. Secondly, there are many elements, e.g. rare gases, halogens and some metalloids, for which the resonance lines or other absorbing lines lie in the far ultraviolet region of the spectrum. In the first case, no absorption occurs because no atoms exist to cause absorption, and in the second, any absorption which does occur is completely swamped by absorption in the flame gases and surrounding atmospheres. Table 4 lists those elements which can be determined using a conventional

TABLE 4.

LIST OF ELEMENTS WHICH CAN OR CANNOT BE DETERMINED BY THE ATOMIC-ABSORPTION FLAME TECHNIQUE

Elements which can be determined	No information available	Elements which cannot be determined
Lithium	Scandium	Hydrogen
*Sodium	Germanium	Helium
*Potassium	Yttrium	Beryllium
Rubidium	Iridium	Boron
*Copper	Tellurium	Carbon
Silver	Rare Earths	Nitrogen
*Gold	Rhenium	Oxygen
*Magnesium	Osmium	Fluorine
*Calcium	Indium	Neon
Strontium	Polonium	Aluminium
Barium	Radium	Silicon
*Zinc	Actinium	Phosphorus
Cadmium	Uranium	Sulphur
Mercury		Chlorine
Tin		Argon
*Lead		Titanium
Chromium		Vanadium
*Manganese		Arsenic
*Iron		Selenium
Cobalt		Bromine
Nickel		Krypton
*Rhodium		Zirconium
*Palladium		Niobium
*Platinum		Iodine
Antimony		Xenon
Bismuth		Hafnium
Caesium		Tungsten
Molybdenum		Radon
Thallium		Thorium
Gallium		

*Detailed applications have been described for determining these elements.

atomizer and flame, and includes those elements which cannot be determined, for reasons already stated. Of those elements in the central column, for which no published information is available, it is likely that at least half of them could be determined by atomic-absorption spectrophotometry.

Because the limit of detection is independent of the detector sensitivity, it is possible to make comparisons between the various flame and atomizer combinations used by different workers. In subsequent sections, where possible, the limits of detection obtained by various workers are quoted, based on an arbitrary limit defined as an optical density of 0·005, or about 1 % absorption.

These sensitivities vary considerably from element to element, from as low as 0·04 ppm for magnesium up to 10 ppm for platinum. It is, of course, possible to detect smaller absorptions but the accuracy of measurement will be very poor because of emission fluctuations from the lamp. No information is available to date on the use of a double-beam instrument where, although absorption will still be the same for a given concentration, it should be possible to make more accurate measurements and thus make use of smaller absorptions.

An alternative to a strictly double-beam method, is the two-line procedure described by Menzies.[45] In this method, the intensity of two lines, emitted from the sharp-line source, are measured simultaneously. One of these lines is an absorption line, the other is used to indicate variations in lamp intensity.

In applying atomic-absorption spectrophotometry to an analytical problem, there are at least eight points to be considered before it can be said that development of a satisfactory method is possible.

5.1 LAMP

The various types of lamps that can be, or have been, used are described in more detail under "Equipment" (page 9). In the determination of most elements, a hollow-cathode lamp is used, with a cathode made from the metal, or alloy of the element, to be determined. The authors have found that multi-purpose cathodes are satisfactory in some instances, for example a lamp with a leaded-brass cathode is suitable for determining copper, zinc and lead. Jones and Walsh,[19] however, maintain that when alloys are used for this purpose, preferential sputtering may take place in the tube, with consequent loss of time before the lamp reaches equilibrium, but we have not found this a serious limitation in the procedures so far investigated.

Laboratory vapour discharge lamps are available for use in determining some elements, particularly sodium and potassium and it is claimed that there is sufficient potassium present as an impurity in a sodium vapour lamp for such a lamp to be used in the determination of potassium.[46]

5.2 ABSORPTION LINE

For each element there are usually several lines which show absorption, but for those elements with simple spectra, the choice is simple. A preliminary experiment, in which each strong line emitted by the lamp is tested, serves to indicate the most suitable line. With complex spectra, such as those obtained from transition elements, a more satisfactory method is that recommended by Allan,[27] in which light emitted by the lamp is passed through a flame and spectra are recorded photographically when distilled water and a solution containing the element under consideration are separately sprayed into the flame. A visual examination of the spectra indicates the absorbing lines, and a few microphotometric measurements, or tests with an atomic-absorption spectrophotometer, serve to indicate which is the most suitable line.

5.3 LAMP CURRENT

Emission characteristics of hollow-cathode and vapour discharge lamps are dependent on operating current and, because lamp emission characteristics can affect absorption, it is necessary to determine the optimum lamp current for each lamp. In general, the lowest current commensurate with a stable and measurable light intensity is used both for hollow-cathode and vapour discharge lamps so that Doppler and pressure broadening are minimized and self-reversal is eliminated. When there is a significant continuous background emission from the lamp, a higher line to background ratio can often be obtained by using a higher operating current. A simple test, using varying lamp currents, is all that is necessary to indicate the best operating current.

5.4 MONOCHROMATOR SLIT-WIDTH

Although monochromator requirements are by no means as stringent as they would be if a continuous source of radiation was used, instead of a hollow-cathode lamp, it is still necessary to investigate the effect of varying band-width. In some instances, when the lamp emits an isolated line with almost no background radiation, e.g. using a sodium vapour lamp, a simple filter is all that is required. Usually, however, a more complex spectrum is emitted from the lamp and it is necessary to use a sufficiently small band-width, or monochromator slit-width, to isolate the required line. If there is any continuous background radiation from the lamp, improved results will be obtained by using the smallest slit width possible, the limitation being the need for a sufficiently large signal for accurate measurement.

5.5 CALIBRATION GRAPH

Using the optimum lamp and monochromator conditions, and aqueous standard solutions, a calibration graph is drawn.

Theoretically, the graph should be a straight line, when optical density and concentration are linear co-ordinates, provided that resonance broadening of the absorption line does not occur (page 7). Almost all calibration graphs are curved towards the concentration axis, and this, in part, may be due to resonance broadening, but Menzies[6] has shown that it could also be due to variations in absorption in different parts of the flame. An alternative cause of curvature may be the measurement of light emitted from the flame when easily excited elements, such as sodium, are being determined using a d.c. light source and measuring system; with an a.c. or a chopped light source, however, this will not occur.

The slope of the calibration graph often changes slightly from day to day, due to variations in atomizer efficiency, and in all subsequent work it is necessary to include tests on a standard solution, in order to apply an appropriate correction to the optical densities measured.

5.6 INTERFERENCES

5.6.1 *Anions*

It is necessary to investigate the interfering effects of various acids, and this is best done in two ways.

Firstly, by testing simple solutions of various acids, it is possible to establish which have absorption properties then, by determining the element under consideration in the presence of various acids, it is possible to demonstrate any interference likely to be introduced by interaction of the particular element with the acid solvent to be used.

Few, if any, interferences are due to the presence of the acid alone, but there is invariably a reduction in absorption when solutions of relatively high acid concentration, and hence higher density and viscosity, are examined, due to the reduced efficiency of the atomizer. Mass action effects cannot be discounted although, in the authors' experience, the only supporting evidence of this has been the effect of acids in determining magnesium in the presence of aluminium (see page 69). The extent to which an acid can be tolerated, without having a significant effect, can be established from a comparison of calibration graphs prepared in the absence and the presence of a range of concentrations of the particular acid. Where the amount of acid necessarily present in the test solution significantly interferes, it is essential to construct a calibration graph using standards with the corresponding acid concentration.

5.6.2 *Cations*

The effect on absorption, due to one element by the presence of other elements, must be investigated. By making determinations in the presence of overwhelming concentrations of other elements, interference effects can readily be established. The number of elements and the relative concentrations of each to be studied will obviously depend upon the purpose for which the procedure is intended; for example, in the examination of inorganic samples for impurities it is advisable to establish the effect of major constituents present in the sample, at concentrations of up to 10,000 times that of the element to be determined.

It is invariably found that with highly concentrated solutions, slight lowering of absorption is obtained; and this is attributed to a reduction in atomizer efficiency due to the increased viscosity of the sample solution (cf. anion interference). With the alkaline earth group elements, cationic interferences are most marked and it is essential to establish the extent of these interferences in the presence of different acids; for example, in the presence of hydrochloric acid, 0·1 g aluminium/ 100 ml suppresses magnesium absorption by 50%, (page 69), but in the presence of sulphuric acid, the suppression is 95% and modifications, similar to those used in emission flame-photometry must be incorporated into the method to circumvent these interferences. This may be achieved either by using standards and samples of identical composition (or nearly so), or by the addition of reagents which have a controlling effect on the interference, the latter, however, may involve a considerable amount of preliminary work if suitable reagents are unknown.

The addition of a known amount of the element to be determined (absorptions are measured before and after the addition) is another possibility, but this method should be used with caution, because ion concentrations may be critical.

5.7 DEVELOPMENT OF METHOD

By combining and applying the optimum conditions, outlined so far, the basis of a method can be obtained, leading to the development of a reliable procedure in which dissolution of the sample and measurement of the absorption is almost all that is involved, apart from the examination of standards. Where interferences occur, and can be overcome by the presence of an added reagent, this usually involves only a simple modification to the procedure.

5.8 ANALYSIS OF SAMPLES

After the method has been developed to this stage, the next step is its application to typical samples containing known amounts of the element to be determined, for example British Chemical Standards or reference samples which have been analysed by alternative reliable procedures. In some instances the simple expedient of preparing solutions of known composition from pure reagents, is a reliable alternative. Replicate tests should be made on several samples, to give an indication of reproducibility; a comparison of the results obtained, with the alternative values, indicates the accuracy attainable. Where the method is to be applied on a routine basis, an indication of the time required to complete single or batch determinations should also be ascertained.

CHAPTER 6

ZINC

To DATE only two papers are known to have been published which deal specifically with the determination of zinc; one, by David[14] is applicable to the analysis of plant materials, the other, by Gidley and Jones[29] deals with the examination of metallurgical samples. Although apparatus used and described in these two papers are markedly different, overall conclusions compare very favourably. David, using a.c. supply to a zinc hollow-cathode lamp, a Hilger medium-spectrograph and a.c. amplification of the photomultiplier output, obtained a sensitivity of 0.25 ppm zinc, whereas Gidley and Jones, using a brass hollow-cathode lamp, in conjunction with a Hilger and Watts attachment to the Uvispek spectrophotometer, and d.c. measurement of the integrated output from the photomultiplier, obtained a sensitivity of 0.1 ppm zinc; both sensitivities corresponding to an optical density of 0.005, or about 1% absorption.

Both publications make reference to the absence of interference by other elements, even when such elements, relative to zinc, are present in an overwhelming excess. David investigated the effects of seven of the elements most likely to occur in plant materials and found no interference and, of the twenty-seven elements examined by Gidley and Jones, only silicon had any significant effect on the zinc absorption. Gidley and Jones also investigated the effect of a two-hundred-fold excess of these twenty-seven elements; the behaviour of two of these, copper and aluminium, both of metallurgical significance, was also examined at even greater concentrations. With concentrations

49

of 1 g of aluminium, or copper, per 100 ml (corresponding to a metal to zinc ratio of 2000 to 1), a slight decrease in the absorption due to zinc was noted and attributed to an increase in viscosity and density of the sample solution, resulting in a reduction in the efficiency of the atomizer.

Almost identical interferences, due to the presence of sulphuric acid, are reported in both publications, and again the reduced absorption due to zinc is attributed to changes in atomizer efficiency. Gidley and Jones reported a serious effect due to the presence of hydrochloric acid; even in the absence of zinc a considerable absorption was observed, not only at the zinc resonance wavelength (Zn 2138 Å) but also at other wavelengths in the region 2100 Å to 2200 Å, corresponding to unidentified hollow-cathode emission lines. Similar effects were also reported using either hydrobromic or hydriodic acids. These interference effects were originally attributed to a molecular absorption band but, because it was not possible to identify such bands by reference to standard books on molecular spectra, some other explanation was sought, and subsequent work carried out in the same laboratory supports an alternative theory.[47]

It was found that when hydrochloric acid was neutralized with sodium hydroxide this interference was eliminated, but when ammonium hydroxide was used for the neutralization, the interference re-occurred. The hollow-cathode emission lines, other than the zinc resonance line, were later identified as copper lines produced by transitions ending in the ground state. (Copper lines were present because a brass hollow-cathode lamp was used.) A possible interpretation of these facts is that the surface oxide layers of the brass burner are attacked by these particular acids or by the relatively volatile ammonium chloride, and reaction products are carried into the flame, thus causing absorption due to both zinc and copper. This explanation is further substantiated in private communications to the authors by David and Walsh who, independently, state that they have not been able to reproduce the hydrochloric acid effect, and it is interesting to note that neither David nor Walsh used brass burners.

Results obtained by David, in the determination of zinc in plant materials, by both atomic-absorption and polarographic procedures, are in good agreement, but David is of the opinion that the atomic-absorption procedure is quicker and less susceptible to interference by other constituents of the sample.

It is the authors' experience that atomic-absorption spectrophotometry is a rapid and accurate means for the direct determination of zinc in metallurgical materials; it is particularly useful because the determination of this metal in these samples, by other procedures, almost invariably necessitates the complete time-consuming removal of major constituents.

An atomic-absorption zinc method is in regular use in the authors' laboratory for the examination of copper, aluminium and zirconium alloys, and an indication of the accuracies obtained is given in Table 5.

The need to determine small amounts of metals, usually in the ppm range, in trade effluents, is increasing in importance and, in this connection, atomic-absorption spectrophotometry is likely to make significant contributions.

As part of a co-operative programme, aimed at providing reliable procedures for the examination of these effluents, three solutions were prepared, containing known amounts of zinc (unknown to the analyst), other metals were also added far in excess of the amounts likely to be encountered in industrial wastes. These additional elements were added for two special reasons, (a) to simulate a possible effluent sample, with respect to zinc and (b) to complicate, almost to an unreasonable extent, the application of conventional chemical procedures, e.g. lead is known to interfere seriously in the dithizone method for determining zinc.

These samples were examined in the authors' laboratory by a straightforward atomic-absorption procedure; no special precautions were taken, the samples were simply atomized and zinc contents were calculated by reference to a calibration graph,

TABLE 5.

ZINC CONTENTS OF COPPER AND ALUMINIUM ALLOYS — VARIOUS PROCEDURES

Sample	Sample number	Method			
		Polaro-graphic	Gravi-metric	Volu-metric	Atomic absorption
		Zinc (%)			
Copper Alloys Copper–zinc alloy (99·5% Cu; nominally 0·5% Zn)	—	—	0·51	—	0·50
Copper–zinc alloy (99·0% Cu; nominally 1·0% Zn)	—	—	1·01	—	1·00
Copper–zinc alloy (98·5% Cu; nominally 1·5% Zn)	—	—	1.56	—	1·53
	J27	0·89	0·90	—	0·91
	E422	0·28	0·33	—	0·29
	E432	0·10	0·11	—	0·097
Everdur alloy*	349	—	0·32	—	0·32
	416	—	0·16	—	0·18
	417	—	0·048	—	0·044
	168	0·72	0·72	—	0·72
	158	0·32	0·31	—	0·32
	512	—	0·02	—	0·017
Phosphor bronze	152	—	0·16	—	0·17
	403	—	0·097	—	0·096
	173	0·058	—	—	0·062
	177	0·27	—	—	0·27
Gilding metal (85% Cu; nominally 15% Zn)	—	—	14·8	—	14·8
Aluminium Alloys	16	—	0·08	—	0·09
	19	—	0·10	—	0·13
Aluminium alloy	21	—	0·26	—	0·25
	24	—	0·76	—	0·77
	30	—	1·01	—	1·02
	1422	—	—	0·12	0·10
Copper–aluminium alloy (50% Cu; 50% Al)	1427	—	—	0·62	0·63
	1428	—	—	0·43	0·41
	1429	—	—	0·66	0·64
Complex alloy (Al/Cu/Mg/Zn)	—	—	4·43	—	4·44

*This alloy contains copper, silicon and manganese

prepared using simple aqueous standard zinc solutions. Results obtained, together with the amounts of zinc added and subsequently disclosed to the analyst, are shown in Table 6.

TABLE 6.

ZINC IN TYPICAL EFFLUENT SAMPLES*

| Sample | Zinc (ppm) | |
	Added	Found
A	7.14	7.1
B	57·1	57·0
C	0·71	0·7

*Supplied by Dr. S. H. Jenkins, Chief Chemist, Birmingham, Tame and Rea District Drainage Board

Sample A contained Cu, Ni, Fe and Cd – each 100 ppm
Sample B contained Hg, Tl, Bi, and Pb – each 50 ppm
Sample C contained Mn, Fe, Co, Ni, Cu and Cd – each 50 ppm.

6.1 METHOD

Full details of the method (and its development) have been published elsewhere[29] and are, therefore, given here in less detail.

The procedure as given below, is for application to a variety of miscellaneous samples, but it is possible, with simple modification, to extend its application to the determination of zinc in almost any material.

6.1.1 Special reagents

Use distilled water throughout and make all dilutions with water, unless otherwise specified.

Standard zinc solutions

Dissolve 1·000 g of high-purity zinc in 100 ml of nitric acid (1 + 1) cool, and dilute to 1 litre. This solution contains 1·0 mg of zinc/ml.

Dilute 100 ml of the previous solution to 1 litre. This solution contains 0·1 mg of zinc/ml.

Separately, dilute 25·0, 50·0, 75·0 and 100 ml aliquots of this solution to 1 litre.

These solutions contain, respectively, 2·5, 5·0, 7·5 and 10·0 μg of zinc/ml, i.e. 2·5, 5·0, 7·5 and 10 ppm of zinc.

Secondary standard zinc solution

Transfer 10·0 ml of the standard solution, containing 0·1 mg of zinc/ml, to a 1 litre calibration flask, and dilute to about 500 ml. Add 50 ml of nitric acid (sp. gr. 1·42) and 50 ml of sulphuric acid (sp. gr. 1·84) mix, and allow to cool. Dilute to the mark, and mix.

This solution contains 1 ppm of zinc in a mixture of nitric (1 + 19) and sulphuric acids (1 + 19).

6.1.2 *Preparation of Mean Standard Graph*

Prepare four standard graphs, using a Hilger atomic-absorption attachment to a Uvispek spectrophotometer with photomultiplier recording. These conditions are applicable in the authors' laboratory, but alternative equipment can be used. When a copper–zinc lamp is used, determine the photomultiplier output current by integration on a capacitor and measure the resulting potential with a bridge valve-voltmeter.[28] Satisfactory instrument settings are:

Lamp current	40 mA
Air pressure to atomizer	15 lb/in²
Wavelength	2138 Å
Integrating capacitor	0·2 μF
Integration period	30 sec
Photomultiplier voltage	1000 V
Slit width	0·18 mm

Switch on the hollow-cathode lamp, light the burner, then switch on the constant voltage supply to the photomultiplier tube. Allow an hour to elapse in order to attain maximum intensity and stability of emission from the hollow-cathode lamp.

Spray water through the atomizer, integrate the photomultiplier output current for 30 sec, and measure the resulting potential (P_0) on the capacitor, using the valve-voltmeter. Spray the standard solutions containing 2·5, 5·0, 7·5 and 10·0 ppm of zinc, in turn, through the atomizer for 30 sec and measure each potential (P_t) as before. Repeat this series of tests ten times.

Calculate the optical density for each standard solution from the expression:

$$\text{Optical density} = \log \frac{P_o}{P_t}$$

and construct graphs relating optical density to zinc content. Scale each curve to a standard optical density for 7·5 ppm of zinc (using the equipment described and the conditions listed above, a standard optical density of 0·3 is suitable). From each of the four curves obtained, record the optical density values corresponding to 1, 2, 3, 4, 5, 6, 7, 8, 9 and 10 ppm of zinc. Average the four values so obtained for each concentration, and draw a mean standard graph from these average values.

6.1.3 Procedures

Sample Weight

The solution to be examined should contain between 1 and 8 ppm of zinc. Suitable sample weights are as follows:

Zinc (%)	0·01/0·08	0·04/0·16	0·10/0·40	0·20/0·80	0·40/1·60
Sample weight (g)	1·0	0·5	0·2	0·1	0·05

In the examination of alloys containing higher percentages of zinc, decrease the weight of sample proportionally; for zinc contents below about 0·01 %, increase the sample weight, e.g. to 5·0 g. Using these large weights of sample, low results may be obtained because of the increased viscosity of the solution over that of the standard solution; this effect, however, can be circumvented by adding to the standard solution an amount of copper, aluminium or other metal equivalent to the weight of total metal in the sample.

Solution of Sample

Copper-base alloys—in the absence of either tin or silicon

Dissolve the sample in 10 ml of nitric acid (1 +1), boil for 1 min, to remove nitrous fumes, cool, and dilute to 100 ml.

Copper-base alloys—tin present

Dissolve the sample in 10 ml hydrochloric acid (1 +1) by the addition of the minimum quantity of nitric acid. Boil to remove nitrous fumes.

Copper-base alloys containing not more than 1% silicon

Dissolve, as described above, and remove silica by filtration.

Copper-base alloys containing more than 1% silicon

Transfer the sample to a platinum dish, and dissolve in 10 ml of nitric acid (1 +1). Add 10 ml of hydrofluoric acid (40 %), 2 ml of sulphuric acid (sp. gr. 1·84) and evaporate until fumes of sulphuric acid are evolved, to remove hydrofluoric acid. Cool, dilute, transfer to a beaker and warm until solution is complete (remove small amounts of lead sulphate by filtration). Transfer the solution to a 100 ml calibrated flask, and dilute to the mark.

Aluminium alloys containing less than 0·5 % *silicon*

Dissolve the sample in 5 ml hydrochloric acid (sp. gr. 1·18) with the aid of hydrogen peroxide added dropwise. Cool and dilute to 100 ml. If there is no further dilution the standard solution used should contain 5 ml of hydrochloric acid also.

Aluminium-base alloys containing more than 0·5% *silicon*

Transfer the sample to a platinum dish, add 10 ml of water, then add, cautiously, hydrofluoric acid (40%) dropwise, until the sample has dissolved. Add a further 5 ml of the hydrofluoric acid, a few drops of nitric acid (sp. gr. 1·42) to dissolve copper, etc., then 2 ml of sulphuric acid (sp. gr. 1·84). Evaporate until fumes of sulphuric acid are evolved, to remove hydrofluoric acid. Cool, dilute, transfer to a beaker, and add 10 ml of nitric acid (1 + 1). Heat until solution is complete, cool, and dilute to 100 ml.

Zirconium-base alloys

Specifications usually limit zinc in these materials to below 0·01%.

Transfer 1·0 g of sample to a platinum dish, add about 5 ml of water, then hydrofluoric acid (40%) dropwise, until the sample has dissolved. Add a few drops of nitric acid (sp. gr. 1·42) to obtain a clear solution, then add 5 ml of sulphuric acid (sp. gr. 1·84). Evaporate under a radiant heater until fumes of sulphuric acid are evolved, cool, dilute, and add 5 ml of nitric acid (sp. gr. 1·42). Transfer to a 150 ml beaker, warm until solution is complete, cool, and dilute to 100 ml.

Note: When atomic-absorption measurements for zinc are made on such a solution, use a secondary standard solution containing 1 ppm of zinc in sulphuric acid (1+19) and nitric acid (1+19).

Miscellaneous materials

Provided that the recommended weight of sample is used, zinc can be determined in most materials by preparing a solution diluted to 100 ml. For solution of the sample it is permissible to use any mineral acid solvent; a preliminary fusion followed by solution of the cooled melt in acid can also be used. Silicon, if present, must be removed by treatment with hydrofluoric and sulphuric acids, as outlined earlier. An appropriate standard solution prepared in the same concentration of acid as that present in the sample solution should, therefore, be used for comparison, as described for the preparation of sample solutions of zirconium and zirconium alloys.

Measurement of absorption

Determine the optical density of the sample solution as described under "Preparation of Mean Standard Graph". Determine the optical density of an appropriate standard zinc solution in conjunction with each batch of samples. Scale the optical density of the standard solution to 0·30 and correct the optical densities of sample solutions proportionally. Read off the amount of zinc in the sample solution by reference to the mean standard graph and calculate the percentage of zinc present in the sample.

Note: If a brass burner is used it is essential to remove halogen acids from solutions to be atomized.

E

CHAPTER 7

LEAD

AT THIS relatively early stage in the development of atomic absorption as an analytical tool, very little has been published on the determination of lead. It has, however, been established, in the authors' laboratory, that atomic-absorption spectrophotometry is invaluable in the determination of lead in a variety of metallurgical materials. In two papers, dealing with atomic absorption in a general way, the limit of detection for lead, using unspecified apparatus, is given as 50[11] and 0·5 ppm.[48] By use of a Hilger and Watts attachment to the Uvispek spectrophotometer, Elwell and Gidley[49] report a detection limit of 2 ppm (corresponding to an optical density of 0·005), in aqueous solution. Robinson[50] claims a limit of 0·5 ppm for lead in gasoline; this favourable sensitivity is, no doubt, due to the presence of an organic medium (see page 31).

The most sensitive line for absorption measurements is Pb 2833 Å, although other lines, e.g. Pb 4057 Å also exhibit absorption. A hollow-cathode lamp using either lead or leaded brass as the cathode material, may be used as the source of sharp-line radiation. Lamps incorporating a *lead* cathode can only be operated at low currents if melting of the metal is to be avoided, although low currents produce narrower emission lines which result in an increase in the measured absorption. With lamps incorporating a *leaded-brass* cathode, higher operating currents can be tolerated and this is an advantage, because the emission line to background ratio increases as the current is raised, and this results in a higher sensitivity when applied to absorption measurements. Table 7 demonstrates this increase of sensitivity with increase in lamp current.

Because of the presence of continuous background and a nearby copper-emission line (Cu 2824 Å), a narrow mono-chromator slit is essential when a leaded-brass hollow-cathode

TABLE 7.

EFFECT OF LAMP CURRENT ON ABSORPTION DUE TO LEAD — LEADED-BRASS HOLLOW-CATHODE LAMP

Lamp current (mA)	Optical density to lead (100 ppm)
10	—
20	0·075
30	0·176
40	0·220
45	0·232
50	0·232

lamp is used. Using a Uvispek monochromator we have established an optimum slit width of 0·1 mm; narrower slits gave insufficient light intensity for accurate measurement.

The determination of lead by atomic absorption is remarkably free from interference by other metals in solution. Robinson[50] has studied the effect of eight metallic elements, and organic sulphur and nitrogen compounds; conclusions reached are that none has any significant interfering effect. Elwell and Gidley[49] report negligible interference by ten of the more common metals associated with non-ferrous materials, even when a twenty-fold excess of the particular metal over lead was present. When very concentrated solutions were used the reduced efficiency of the atomizer was again apparent (cf. zinc, page 50) but this presented no problem, because comparable standards could easily be prepared.

One observation, for which no simple explanation has been put forward, was made when traces of lead were determined in a concentrated solution of iron or steel (using a leaded-brass hollow-cathode lamp).

With a solution of high purity iron (lead less than 0·001 %) in hydrochloric acid (2 g iron/100 ml), an absorption corresponding to an optical density of 0·025 was obtained, using the lead absorption line wavelength (2833 Å) (equivalent to 0·05 % lead in the sample). No absorption was detected at the wavelength of the nearby copper line (2824 Å), thus eliminating the possibility of an absorption band in that wavelength region. (Cu 2824 Å would not exhibit atomic absorption even when copper atoms were present in the flame because the emission line does not terminate in the ground state). When copper solutions were examined in the same way, no absorption was found at either wavelength, even with solutions containing up to 5 g copper/100 ml.

In the authors' published paper,[49] a method is described for determining lead in a range of ferrous and non-ferrous materials, using appropriate standards to overcome effects due to the use of concentrated solutions and to variations in atomizer efficiencies. Tables 8 and 9 show the accuracy that can be achieved with this procedure, which can be extended to the examination of aluminium-base alloys and to the determination of lead contents lower than is indicated in these tables, for example, lead down to about 0·02 % can be determined in copper-base alloys. Because of its freedom from inter-element interferences, the method can also be applied to the determination of lead in other materials, e.g. highly alloyed steels, etc. In the examination of several 13 % chrome steel samples, the authors have confirmed lead contents of <0·005 %, by an atomic-absorption procedure. In the metallurgical applications referred to in the tables, the advantage of atomic-absorption procedures, over alternative methods, lies in the speed with which results of comparable, and sometimes improved, accuracy can be obtained.

TABLE 8.

LEAD IN COPPER ALLOYS

Sample	Lead (%)	
	Chemical	Atomic absorption
B.C.S. No. 183 Bronze A	1·83*	1·81, 1·81
,, No. 179 Manganese Brass B	0·78*	0·77, 0·79
,, No. 207 Bronze C	0·41*	0·41, 0·42
ICI Reference Standard Brass No. 7	3·55	3·52, 3·55
Leaded Brass XR.2	1·77, 1·78	1·77, 1·77
,, ,, XR.4	1·02, 1·03	1·02, 1·01
,, ,, XR.11	2·10, 2·14	2·13, 2·14
,, ,, XR.38	0·37, 0·38	0·39, 0·40
,, ,, XR.39	3·19, 3·19	3·19, 3·20

*Certificate value

TABLE 9.

LEAD IN LEADED STEELS

Sample	Lead (%)	
	Chemical*	Atomic absorption
163	0·280	0·277, 0·287
196A	0·175	0·182, 0·185
257A	0·076	0·080, 0·070
195	0·175	0·185
272	0·115	0·125
274	0·185	0·195
X	0·28	0·282, 0·280
B.C.S. No. 212/1	0·22†	0·215, 0·215

*Preliminary separation of lead as sulphide, followed by conversion to, and weighing as, lead molybdate.
†Certificate value

7.1 METHOD

Full details of the method (and its development) have been published elsewhere[49] and are, therefore, given here in less detail.

Equipment and operational details are similar to those given under Zinc (page 53) except that instantaneous-intensity readings are made.

7.1.1 *Special reagents*

Use distilled water throughout, and make all dilutions with water, unless otherwise specified.

Acid mixture

To about 300 ml of water add 300 ml of nitric acid (sp. gr. 1·42). Add 200 ml of hydrochloric acid (sp. gr. 1·16–1·18), cool, and dilute to 1 litre.

Standard lead solution

Weigh, as accurately as possible, 0·5 g of pure lead (e.g. British Chemical Standard No. 210b) and dissolve in the minimum volume of nitric acid (1 + 1). Cool and dilute to 1 litre.

1 ml ≡ 0·5 mg lead

Standard copper/lead solution A

Dissolve 10·00 g of high purity copper in 100 ml of acid mixture. Cool, add 200·0 ml of the standard lead solution, and dilute to 1 litre.

1 ml ≡ 100 μg lead (100 ppm Pb)

Standard copper/lead solution B

Dissolve 5·00 g of high purity copper in 50 ml of acid mixture. Cool, add 200·0 ml of the standard lead solution, and dilute to 1 litre.

1 ml ≡ 100 μg lead (100 ppm Pb)

Standard iron solution

Dissolve 2·00 g of high purity iron (e.g. H.H.P. iron) in 20 ml of hydrochloric acid (sp. gr. 1·16–1·18) and oxidize with 1–2 ml of nitric acid (sp. gr. 1·42), added dropwise. Cool, and dilute to 100 ml.

Standard iron/lead solution

Dissolve 2·00 g of high purity iron (e.g. H.H.P. iron) in 20 ml of hydrochloric acid (sp. gr. 1·16–1·18) and oxidize with 1–2 ml of nitric acid (sp. gr. 1·42), added dropwise. Add 10 ml of standard lead solution, and dilute to 100 ml.

1 ml ≡ 50 μg lead (0·25 % Pb in iron)

7.1.2 *Preparation of Mean Standard Graph*

To each of five 100 ml calibrated flasks add, separately, 5·0, 10·0, 20·0, 30·0 and 40·0 ml of the standard lead solution and dilute each to the mark. These solutions contain 25, 50, 100, 150 and 200 ppm lead respectively.

Instrument settings, using a leaded-brass hollow-cathode lamp, are as follows:

Lamp current	40 mA
Atomizer air pressure	15 lb/in²
Wavelength	2833 Å
Photomultiplier voltage	1100 V
Slit width	0·10 mm

Use the same operational procedure as given for the determination of zinc (page 54) and calculate the optical density for each standard solution. Scale each curve to an optical density of 0·22 to 100 ppm lead. Take the average readings for each of three curves and plot these as the final mean standard graph.

7.1.3 Procedure

Copper-Base Alloys

Sample weight and volume of acid solvent mixture

Lead content (%)	Sample (g)	Acid solvent mixture (ml)
0·1–1·0	1·0	10
1·0–3·5	0.5	5

Dissolve the recommended weight of sample in the appropriate volume of acid solvent mixture, boil, to expel nitrous fumes, cool and dilute to 100 ml in a calibrated flask.

Determine the optical density of the sample solution as described under "Preparation of Mean Standard Graph". Determine the optical density of the appropriate standard copper/lead solution in conjunction with each batch of samples, i.e. solution A for 1 g samples and solution B for 0·5 g samples (Note).

Scale the optical density of the standard solution to 0·22 and correct the optical densities of the sample solutions proportionally. Read off the amount of lead in the sample solution by reference to the mean standard curve and calculate the percentage of lead in the sample.

Note: The appropriate standard solution corresponding to the sample weight must be used to compensate for any variation in viscosity of the atomized solution.

Steels

Dissolve 2·00 g of the sample in 20 ml of hydrochloric acid (sp. gr. 1·16–1·18) then oxidize with 1–2 ml of nitric acid (sp. gr. 1·42), added dropwise. Filter off any precipitated silica, wash the filter thoroughly with water, then dilute the filtrate to 100 ml.

Use the same instrument settings and setting up procedure as described under "Preparation of Mean Standard Graph" and determine the optical density of the standard and sample solutions. Prepare a calibration graph by drawing a straight line through the two points obtained for the two standard iron solutions, read off the amount of lead in the sample solution by reference to this curve and calculate the percentage of lead in the sample.

CHAPTER 8

MAGNESIUM

SEVERAL papers dealing with the determination of magnesium in a variety of materials have been published. One, by Allen[12] dealing with the principles of atomic-absorption spectrophotometry, refers specifically to magnesium determinations. Menzies[6] comments on some apparently anomalous effects, and subsequently refers to some of the authors', otherwise unpublished, data. David[14] gives details of the analysis of plant and soil extracts, and Willis[51] describes the determination of magnesium in blood serum. In the authors' laboratory a procedure for determining magnesium in aluminium alloys has been developed and is in regular use.

A common feature of all published work on the determination of magnesium by atomic-absorption spectrophotometry is the reference to interference by other elements (or compounds) on magnesium absorption. These interferences have been circumvented either by controlling the amount of interfering elements, or by adding a suppressing agent, e.g. salts of strontium, lanthanum or ethylenediaminetetracetic acid. The mechanism of interference and suppression of interference is not fully understood, although it is almost certainly associated with the formation of stable magnesium compounds which are not completely dissociated in the flame. A more detailed discussion of this problem appears on page 28.

Only one magnesium line (2852 Å) is suitable for absorption measurements and hollow-cathode lamps with either magnesium or aluminium/magnesium-alloy cathodes have been used. To obtain maximum sensitivity it is necessary to operate magnesium-cathode lamps at low currents (not exceeding about 10 mA), at higher currents excessive line broadening leads to a reduction in absorption. With aluminium/magnesium-lamps, however, higher currents (up to 40 mA) are necessary to obtain maximum sensitivity because of the increased line to background intensity ratio. Various limits of magnesium detection are reported, e.g. Willis[51] implies a value of 0·01 ppm; in the authors' work, the limit is higher by a factor of about four, which is nearer the limit of 0·1 ppm quoted by other workers.[6, 8, 12]

8.1 INTERFERENCES

The most serious interferences occur when magnesium is to be determined in the presence of other elements capable of forming acidic oxides which are stable at high temperatures. Table 10 shows the effect of various elements on the determination of magnesium.

TABLE 10.

EFFECT OF VARIOUS ELEMENTS ON THE DETERMINATION OF MAGNESIUM (6 ppm Mg in presence of 1000 ppm of a second element)

Added	Found Magnesium (ppm)
Aluminium	0·30
Silicon	1·02
Titanium	1·56
Zirconium	3·60
Hafnium	3·00
Thorium	6·10
Strontium	9·20

Because of the wide range of interfering elements, it is not possible to detail methods for overcoming all interferences, but a description of the development of an atomic-absorption procedure in the authors' laboratory, magnesium in aluminium alloys, will indicate a possible method of approach to similar problems.

8.2 ALUMINIUM ALLOYS

It was evident, from Table 8, that aluminium seriously interfered in this determination; this interference was, therefore, examined in detail.

A variation in acid concentration had a considerable effect on magnesium absorption, in the presence of aluminium (Fig. 6). With the addition of increasing amounts of either nitric or sulphuric acid, there was a steep drop in magnesium absorption until a constant (very low) level was obtained, after which no further decrease in absorption was observed. In the presence of hydrochloric acid, however, there was a gradual increase in

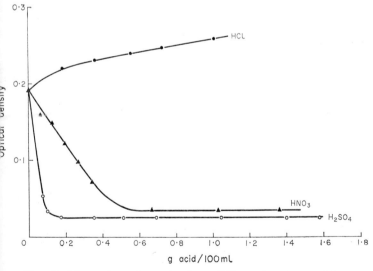

FIG. 6. Magnesium determination — Effect of various acids on aluminium interference. $5\mu g$ magnesium/ml and $0\cdot2$ g aluminium/100 ml present.

absorption as the acidity was increased over the range of concentrations examined. In all these experiments, absorptions were much lower than those obtained in the absence of aluminium.

The differing effects of chloride and sulphate ions on the interference due to aluminium, have been independently observed by Menzies[6].

Following emission flame-photometric practice, where similar interferences are controlled by the addition of strontium,[52] the effect of adding varying amounts of a strontium salt to aluminium/magnesium solutions was investigated. Results obtained (Fig. 7) showed that considerable variations in magnesium absorption occurred with varying amounts of aluminium, in the presence of 0·25 and 0·5 g strontium/100 ml. When the concentration of strontium was increased to 0·75 g/100 ml, the supprerssing effect of aluminium was reasonably constant for aluminium levels of from 0·05 to 0·25 g/100 ml, and this information was used in the development of the method.

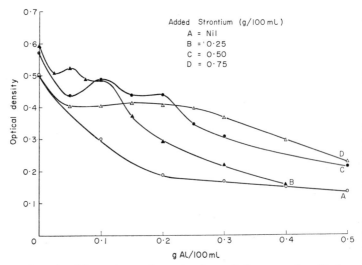

FIG. 7. Magnesium determination — Influence of added strontium on aluminium interference. 5 μg magnesium/ml present.

It had been demonstrated that the presence of strontium controlled interference due to aluminium, but it was necessary to show that strontium continued as a suppressor in the presence of other elements likely to be present, and also in solutions of variable acidity. Accordingly, tests were carried out separately in the presence of nitric acid, hydrochloric acid and silicon; sulphuric acid was not used because this would have precipitated strontium sulphate. Hydrochloric acid and nitric acid, up to 1·0 and 1·8 g/100 ml respectively, caused no interference. A hundred-fold excess of silicon over magnesium reduced the magnesium absorption by about 10%; for most practical purposes, therefore, interference by silicon can be ignored.

With this information, the basis of a method for determining magnesium in aluminium alloys was provided.

8.3 OUTLINE OF PROCEDURE (MAGNESIUM IN ALUMINIUM ALLOYS) AND RESULTS

A known weight of sample was dissolved in hydrochloric acid, with the aid of hydrogen peroxide, added dropwise. After adding a known volume of standard strontium solution, the test solution was diluted to a convenient volume and magnesium was determined (the reference calibration curve was based on standards containing aluminium and strontium in proportion to the amounts of these elements present in the sample solution). When the magnesium content of the sample was higher than that covered by the calibration curve, a smaller sample weight was taken and aluminium solution was added, so that the aluminium contents of the test and standard solutions, used in preparing the calibration curve, were the same. Details of the method finally used are given later.

Several British Chemical Standard alloys were analysed by this procedure and results obtained are shown in Table 11, together with corresponding certified magnesium values. The good agreement indicates that accurate results can be obtained by the atomic-absorption method.

TABLE 11.

MAGNESIUM IN ALUMINIUM ALLOYS

Sample	Magnesium (%)	
	Certificate value	Atomic absorption
B.C.S. No. 263*	4·23	4·35
„ No. 216†	0·53	0·56
„ No. 216/1†	0·74	0·75

*Also contains 0·13 % copper, 0·49 % manganese, 0·15 % silicon, and 0·41 % iron. †Duralumin alloy 216/1 also contains 4·42 % copper, 0·73 % manganese, 0·74 % silicon, and 0·40 % iron.

Provided that all standard solutions are ready, a single sample can be analysed by one analyst in 30 min, as opposed to $1\frac{1}{2}$ days by a typical chemical procedure, and up to 30 samples can be analysed in 8 hours. The accuracy of the absorption measurement is about 2 %, expressed as a coefficient of variation, but a higher precision can be obtained by making replicate measurements. Accuracy of the determination is also dependent on the control of interfering elements, and experience has shown that this alone can introduce errors of about 2–3 % of the magnesium content. The method is, therefore, satisfactory for all magnesium determinations below about 1 %, but at much higher levels, the method is more suitable for identification purposes.

8.4 DISCUSSION

Although the method of dealing with interference will vary with each particular problem, in principle, the approach is likely to be the same.

According to Walsh,[3] interferences observed are not due to changes in flame characteristics, and experiments were made to confirm this statement. An additional atomizer was added to the unit and fine spray from two independent atomizers was combined at the base of the burner tube. (In this way, droplets from the two separate atomizers would be thoroughly mixed, but should not coalesce.) One atomizer sprayed a solution of magnesium, the other a solution containing aluminium. No interference in the magnesium absorption was observed, but in a second series of tests, when distilled water was sprayed from one atomizer and a solution containing both magnesium and aluminium from the other, serious interference occurred. It was also found that strontium only acted as a suppressor when the salt was in the same solution as the aluminium and magnesium. When strontium was sprayed from a separate atomizer, it had no influence on the suppression effect of aluminium. (This experimental work was done just prior to the publication of similar conclusions by Fukushima et al.[53] who obtained similar results on an extensive series of tests using emission measurements.)

Interferences, similar to those to which reference has just been made, are observed in emission flame-photometry and it is generally accepted that they are due to the formation of a stable compound in which both magnesium and aluminium are present. In the double atomizer experiments, aluminium and magnesium droplets exist separately, and at no time do these independent droplets come sufficiently close to each other to enable a stable aluminium/magnesium compound to be formed; only when the two metals are present in the same solution do they subsequently interact.

From a study of the effects of various acids in relation to interference by aluminium, it is possible that the stable aluminium/magnesium compound is a mixed oxide. Magnesium and aluminium nitrates, or sulphates, undergo simple thermal decomposition into their respective oxides and, because they will be in intimate contact with each other, in a single solution, conditions for the formation of a stable mixed oxide, are favourable. When these metals are present as chlorides, however, their salts must first dissociate, before being oxidized, thus,

F

for a short time, some free magnesium atoms may exist and give rise to atomic absorption.

In the presence of strontium, a preferential reaction with aluminium takes place leaving magnesium compounds free to dissociate in the flame, a theory which is substantiated by the shape of curves showing the effect of added strontium (Fig. 7). For example, above certain aluminium to strontium ratios (0·1 g aluminium/100 ml in the presence of 0·25 g strontium/100 ml and 0·2 g aluminium/100 ml when 0·5 g strontium/100 ml is present) an increase in aluminium concentration results in a very rapid drop in absorption. These ratios correspond to a state of equilibrium between strontium and aluminium. When the aluminium concentration is increased, excess aluminium is free to react with magnesium and low magnesium absorptions are obtained.

8.5 METHOD (MAGNESIUM IN ALUMINIUM ALLOYS)

Equipment used and operational details are the same as those given under zinc (page 54).

8.5.1 *Special reagents*

Use distilled water throughout, and make all dilutions with water, unless otherwise specified.

Aluminium solution

Weigh, as accurately as possible, 10 g of high purity aluminium and dissolve in 50 ml of hydrochloric acid (sp. gr. 1·16–1·18), with the aid of hydrogen peroxide, added dropwise. Cool, and dilute to 1 litre.

1 ml ≡ 10·0 mg aluminium

Strontium nitrate solution

Dissolve 85·39 g of strontium nitrate in water and dilute to 1 litre.

15 ml ≡ 0·75 g strontium

Standard magnesium solution

Weigh, as accurately as possible, 0·1 g of high purity magnesium (e.g. H.H.P. magnesium) and dissolve in the minimum volume of nitric acid (1 +1). Cool, and dilute to 1 litre.

1 ml ≡ 0·10 mg magnesium

Standard mixed solution A

Transfer 100·0 ml of the aluminium solution, 150·0 ml of the strontium nitrate solution and 50·0 ml of the standard magnesium solution to a 1 litre calibrated flask, and dilute to the mark.

8.5.2 *Preparation of Mean Standard Graph*

To each of five 100 ml calibrated flasks add, separately, 2·0, 4·0, 6·0, 8·0 and 10·0 ml of the standard magnesium solution. To each flask add 10·0 ml of the aluminium solution, 15·0 ml of the strontium nitrate solution, then dilute to the mark. These solutions contain 2·0, 4·0, 6·0, 8·0 and 10·0 ppm magnesium, respectively.

Instrument settings, using an aluminium/magnesium hollow-cathode lamp, are as follows:

Lamp current	40 mA
Atomizer air pressure	15 lb/in²
Wavelength	2852 Å
Photomultiplier voltage	960 V
Slit width	0·10 mm

Use the same operational procedure as that given for the determination of zinc; calculate the optical density for each standard solution. Scale each curve to an optical density of 0·50 for 5 μg magnesium/ml, take the average readings for each of the three curves and plot these as the final mean standard graph.

8.5.3 *Procedure*

Magnesium content	Sample weight
(%)	(g)
0·1–1·0	1·0
1·0–5·0	0·1

Dissolve the recommended weight of sample in 5 ml of hydrochloric acid (sp. gr. 1·16–1·18), with the aid of hydrogen peroxide, added dropwise. Cool, and dilute to 100 ml in a calibrated flask. Transfer a 10 ml aliquot into a second 100 ml calibrated flask and add 15·0 ml of the strontium nitrate solution. If the smaller sample weight is used, adjust the aluminium content of the solution to 0·1 g/100 ml, by the addition of 9·0 ml of the standard aluminium solution. Dilute to the mark.

Determine the optical density as described under "Preparation of Mean Standard Graph". Determine the optical density of the standard mixed solution A in conjunction with each batch of samples.

Scale the optical density of the standard solution to 0·50 and correct the optical density of the sample solutions proportionally. Read off the amount of magnesium in the sample solution by reference to the mean standard graph and calculate the magnesium content in the sample.

CHAPTER 9

MANGANESE

A PAPER by Allan[27] describes the determination of iron and manganese, with particular reference to the analysis of materials of agricultural interest.

Because of the complex nature of the manganese emission spectrum and the presence of multiple ground state lines, choice of the most sensitive line for absorption measurement is difficult, but Allan's photographic procedure[27] overcomes this problem. He placed a burner between a hollow-cathode lamp and a spectrograph so that the light from the lamp passed through the burner before entering the spectrograph. A series of exposures was then made when distilled water and several standard solutions containing various amounts of manganese were sprayed into the flame. A similar series of spectrograms of the emission from the flame alone was also recorded on the same photographic plate, so that corrections could be made for emission (if any) due to manganese from the flame. The photographic plates were calibrated in the conventional way and microphotometric measurements of line intensities in the various spectra were made. By comparing lines in the spectra, obtained when distilled water was sprayed, with those obtained when manganese solutions were sprayed, a measure of the absorption could be obtained. With the lamp, initially used by Allan, the only lines he observed ending in the ground state were those from the two strongest multiplets. Emission from the flame was observed at 4030 Å, but at 2800 Å, no flame emission radiation was detected. The measured absorption, however, was ten times greater at 2800 Å than at 4030 Å, even when corrections for the flame emission radiation were made. Of the three lines constituting the multiplet at 2800 Å, the line with the highest lamp emission intensity (2794·8 Å) also showed the highest absorption.

Allan used this photographic procedure for ascertaining which line exhibits the greatest absorption, but in his subsequent work, photoelectric detection was used. With an air/acetylene burner and a manganese/copper hollow-cathode lamp, Allan obtained a

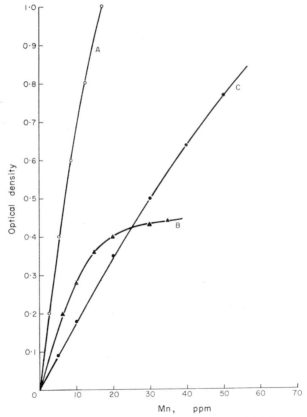

Fig. 8. Calibration curves obtained using Mn 2794·8 Å
    A. Allan, using photographic measurement.
    B. Allan, using photoelectric measurement.
    C. Elwell and Gidley using photoelectric measurement.

severely curved calibration curve, whereas using photographic measurements, a much steeper and straighter calibration curve was found (Fig. 8). The curved calibration curve was due to the high background intensity obtained from that particular lamp; photographic measurements being much less affected by background radiation.

In a footnote to his paper, Allan states that with other lamps, in particular one produced by Walsh (details of lamp production are given by Jones and Walsh[19]), a calibration curve similar to that obtained photographically, also applied to photoelectric recording. Using the equipment described by Gidley and Jones,[29] a reasonably straight calibration graph, but of lower slope than Allan's photographic curve (Fig. 8), can be obtained. This difference in slope is possibly due to using an air/coal-gas flame, which is cooler than the air/acetylene flame used by Allan.

Allan used absorption measurements for determining manganese in agricultural materials, and showed that the presence of large amounts of sodium, potassium, calcium, magnesium or phosphorus (500 ppm–3000 ppm) had no effect on the absorption due to 10 ppm manganese.

The authors have examined possible applications of atomic absorption to metallurgical analysis, and found that a large excess of sodium, potassium, copper, lead, iron, nickel, tin or zinc had no significant effect on manganese absorption but that calcium, magnesium, aluminium, titanium and zirconium caused a slight reduction of the measured absorption; the presence of silicon caused a very marked lowering of absorption. In each of these tests, a solution containing 20 ppm of manganese was examined in the presence of 1000 ppm of the second element under examination.

The accuracy of this determination is indicated by results quoted by Allan who obtained recoveries of between 99–103 % manganese in the examination of agricultural samples. Table 12 shows some results obtained by the authors when the method was applied to various metallurgical materials. The method used was similar to that given in detail under zinc (page 53), using comparison standards containing an equivalent amount of the matrix element corresponding to the weight of sample taken. In this way any slight interference or effects due to changes in atomizer efficiency were circumvented.

Allan[27] states that, although the method is not as sensitive as some colorimetric methods, it is particularly attractive because of its rapidity, simplicity and freedom from interference. However, the method does not appear to offer any outstanding advantages in these respects over existing colorimetric methods.

TABLE 12.

MANGANESE IN VARIOUS METALLURGICAL MATERIALS

Sample	Manganese (%)	
	Chemical	Atomic absorption
Titanium Alloy Ti/1·5 % Al/1·5 % Mn	1·41	1·45, 1·46
Steel (low alloyed) B.C.S. No. 256	1·21*	1·21, 1·20
„ No. 233	0·24*	0·22, 0·24
Copper-Base 526 Manganese Bronze	1·51	1·57, 1·58
623 „ „	1·57	1·53, 1·55
288 „ „	1·57	1·56, 1·58
B.C.S. No. 179 — Mangan- nese Brass B	1·03*	1·04, 1·06

*Certificate value

CHAPTER 10

IRON

IN THE section dealing with the determination of manganese, reference is made to a paper by Allan[27] in which he describes the determination of iron and manganese, with particular reference to the analysis of agricultural materials. Many of the comments made for manganese (page 77), apply equally to the determination of iron.

The emission spectrum from an iron hollow-cathode lamp is very complex, and Allan used a photographic method to establish the most sensitive absorption lines for determining this metal. Allan found that the most sensitive absorption lines were 2483, 2488 and 2522 Å, the limit of detection being about 0·1–1·2 ppm, using a 12 cm long × 0·07 cm wide air/acetylene flame. At these wavelengths, practically no emission from the flame was observed and this enabled a simple arrangement of lamp, flame and monochromator to be used.

Because the iron emission spectrum is very complex, interference due to nearby non-absorbing lines may be serious. Allan reports a difference between the calibration curves obtained from photographic and photoelectric measurements, and ascribes this to the interfering effects of nearby non-absorbing lines. These effects may be largely overcome by setting a zero intensity with a concentrated iron solution, thus backing off the constant non-absorbing portion of the radiation reaching the photocell.

According to Allan, the presence of a considerable excess of potassium, calcium, sodium, magnesium or phosphorus has no effect on absorption due to iron, but we have found, using a cool air/coal-gas flame, that several elements interfere. Recoveries of between 80 and 90 % were obtained when a solution containing 50 ppm of iron was examined in the presence of 1000 ppm of calcium, copper, aluminium, titanium or zirconium; in the presence of a similar amount of silicon, only 26 % of the iron was recovered.

Because several reliable, sensitive colorimetric methods are available for determining iron, and in view of the observations to which reference has just been made, atomic-absorption procedures are not likely to be applied to the determination of this metal. Allan, however, suggests that for the analysis of agricultural materials the determination of iron by an atomic-absorption method is preferable to colorimetric methods, because of its rapidity, simplicity and freedom from interference; an opinion which is open to comment.

CHAPTER 11

CALCIUM

METHODS for determining calcium in agricultural and biological materials have been described by David [26, 54] and Willis [37, 55, 56] respectively. Both authors refer to interferences which are likely to occur, particularly those due to the presence of phosphate, aluminium, sodium or protein. These interferences can be overcome by (a) making additions of other salts which suppress the interference, (b) removing the interfering element or (c) simulating the composition of the sample in the standards. A general discussion on these interferences, and means for overcoming them in both emission and absorption measurements, is given earlier (page 28).

Both David and Willis use calcium hollow-cathode lamps and air/acetylene flames. Using the calcium resonance line 4227 Å, (flame length 2·7 cm) David [26] obtained a detection limit of 1 ppm, but Willis [37] with a 10 cm flame, claims a ten times greater sensitivity. This difference cannot be due entirely to the difference in flame length, because other factors which are not specified, such as atomizer efficiency and flame temperature, also influence sensitivity.

Flame conditions are critical if the highest sensitivities are to be achieved. Willis [37] has shown that with an air/coal-gas flame, the concentration of free calcium atoms is low in the upper part of the flame and highest just above the zone of unburnt gas. Further, a rich gas/air mixture had to be used in order to obtain the highest concentration of calcium atoms. It was found, however, that the calcium absorption was very susceptible to suppression by phosphorus in the air/coal-gas flame but, using an air/acetylene flame, this was more easily controlled. As with the air/coal-gas flame, the concentration of calcium atoms was highest near to the base of the flame and for optimum sensitivity a rich gas/air mixture was necessary. David[26] has also demonstrated this effect by measuring absorption at different heights in the flame; a maximum absorption was obtained 5 mm above the burner top, i.e. just above the cone of unburnt gas.

The method of measuring absorption, used by both Willis and David, is to focus a reduced image of the hollow-cathode discharge in the centre of the flame; to obtain maximum sensitivity, the position of this image is critical. David[26] details all the variables, namely air and gas-flow rates, and the height of the image above the burner top, but Willis suggests fixing the air pressure and the height of the image above the burner, and varying the gas flow until maximum absorption is obtained.

It is impossible to separate light originating from the hollow-cathode lamp from the emission of the flame, by optical means, because of the focusing system, and it is essential to use an alternative method for eliminating the effect of flame emission; both authors use a modulated lamp supply (50 c/s or 100 c/s) and an a.c. amplifier. In addition, the design of the burner is important because, with a Meker-type burner, the region of maximum sensitivity will be at varying heights above the burner, due to the presence of individual blue cones in the flame. A burner, as described by Willis[56] or Clinton[40], with a slot aperture is preferable, because the region of maximum sensitivity will be at a constant height above the burner.

David has investigated interferences introduced by certain elements and has found that if measurements are made in the presence of sulphuric acid (1+49) and 6 mg magnesium/ml, no interferences occurred with concentrations of up to 200 ppm phosphorus, 80 ppm aluminium or 40 ppm silicon. Small amounts of sodium or potassium caused an enhancement of absorption but, by making additions of 200 ppm sodium and 1500 ppm potassium, these effects were eliminated.

In the examination of blood serum, Willis found that sodium, phosphorus and protein interfered, and compensated for interference due to sodium by adding a known amount of sodium chloride to the reference solution; for the elimination of protein and phosphorus interferences, he used several alternative procedures.

Separation of calcium by precipitation as oxalate was not recommended, because of the apparent incomplete removal of calcium from serum.[57] The most accurate calcium results were obtained on serum using trichloracetic acid to react with the protein, in the presence of either strontium or lanthanum to suppress interference by phosphorus. More rapid results of acceptable accuracy have been obtained, following simple dilution of the serum, either with water (the presence of protein largely offsets the phosphorus interference) or a solution of the sodium salt of EDTA.

With urine samples,[56] interference by the large concentration of phosphorus present, has been overcome by adding either strontium or lanthanum chloride, which also eliminated the effect of two-hundred-fold excess of sodium or potassium.

Willis[37] noted that the interference of phosphorus was very similar to that described by Strasheim and Nell,[58] and David[26] also comments that phosphorus and aluminium interferences are similiar in both emission and absorption work. Similar methods to those described by Willis, for overcoming these interferences in serum samples, have also been used in emission flame-photometry.[59] It appears, therefore, that in determining calcium, there is no obvious advantage in using an atomic absorption rather than an emission method, because both methods have about the same sensitivity.[60] When, however, a multi-cathode lamp is available, so that calcium and other elements can be made on a single sample, with the same equipment and with a minimum of difficulty, an atomic-absorption method may be preferred. Willis[56] describes one such example where both calcium and magnesium determinations are made on the same sample.

CHAPTER 12

SODIUM

OF the element determined by emission-flame photometry sodium is the most sensitive; it also has a high sensitivity in atomic-absorption spectrophotometry. Several workers have investigated the determination of sodium, and detection limits have been reported ranging from 0·05 ppm (David[54] and Willis[61]) to 0·5 ppm (Robinson[31]); using a very simple filter-instrument in our own laboratory we have attained a detection limit of 0·1 ppm. Other references to this determination include a detailed description of a precision instrument, using a null-point method[62] and, in a further reference,[63] application of the method to the analysis of biological culture solutions is discussed. In neither of these two papers is sufficient information available to deduce limits of detection, but Malmstadt and Chambers[62] demonstrate that "high" accuracies can be attained in determinations involving sodium in the 1–100 ppm range.

The source of sharp-line radiation is usually a vapour discharge lamp,[54, 31, 62, 63] but Willis,[61] has also used a hollow-cathode lamp. In the authors' laboratory advantages have been shown of running a vapour-discharge lamp at a current lower than that normally specified by the makers (page 11), to reduce line broadening and the degree of self-reversal in the lamp. Monochromators[31, 54, 61] and filters[62, 63] have both been used for isolating the yellow sodium D line, in fact, it is possible to eliminate a wavelength selection system because the light output from a sodium-vapour discharge-lamp is almost entirely restricted to the yellow D lines. When a monochromator is not used, it is possible to use a very simple detector and measuring system; all that is required is a selenium barrier-layer photocell and a galvanometer.

Because of the high emission sensitivity of sodium, the problem of measuring the intensity of the absorbed radiation, without interference by emission from the flame, is most pronounced. A simple lens system in which an image of the discharge lamp is thrown on to the photocell, at the same time defocusing the flame emission, is entirely adequate for determining sodium in the 0·1–20 ppm range, but if higher levels of sodium are to be determined, the calibration curve is less steep and results inaccurate. Modulation of the light source and use of a.c. detectors completely overcome this interference. A simple instrument, the Si-Ro-Spec, using an a.c. vapour discharge lamp and filter for wavelength selection has been described,[64] and is claimed to be free from scattered light and background interference, both of which can be troublesome with filter emission flame-photometry.

David[54] states that the presence of phosphate, aluminium, sulphate and silicate, at concentrations each in excess of that normally found in soil extracts, had no effect on the absorption due to sodium; Willis[61] found that the components of blood serum did not interfere with the sodium determination. Both Malmstadt and Chambers[62] and Robinson[31] state that mineral acids (hydrochloric or sulphuric) affected determined sodium values, but gave no indication of the extent of these interferences.

Because of the relatively high concentration of sodium in blood serum (over 3500 ppm), Willis[61] has devised means for reducing the sensitivity of the atomic-absorption procedure; using a 10 cm burner and the 5890 Å resonance doublet, measurements could be made in the 0–10 ppm range. By turning the burner through an angle of 90°, the light-path was reduced to about 0·5 cm, and solutions containing up to 200 ppm could be measured using the 5890 Å doublet. Using the second resonance doublet 3302 Å, 3303 Å, for which the oscillator strengths are only 0·014 of those for the 5890 Å doublet, higher concentrations of sodium (up to 1000 ppm) could be measured using the normal 10 cm flame. Using these higher sodium concentrations it was possible to use the same solution for other determinations and, at the same time, reduce the ever-present risk of unintentional contamination with sodium.

From evidence available it seems that, in general, interferences in both emission and atomic absorption are similar. If a filter photometer is used for emission measurements, interferences from background and nearby lines occur; in atomic absorption this is entirely overcome, even with a simple filter instrument.

Although most emission methods are more sensitive for determining sodium, this is not a very important factor, because of the high sensitivity of both methods. Further, there are considerable difficulties in avoiding spurious results at very low sodium concentrations. Thus, there is very little to choose between emission and absorption methods (except when using filter instruments) and hence the choice of method is mainly dependent on available equipment.

G

CHAPTER 13

POTASSIUM

SEVERAL papers dealing with the determination of sodium also provide for the determination of potassium. David[54] and Willis[61] give details of their methods for determining potassium in agricultural and biological materials respectively, and Malmstadt and Chambers[62] describe a high-precision procedure, using a null-point method. The limit of detection for potassium is about half that for sodium, namely 0·1–0·2 ppm, using the principal resonance doublet at 7665 Å and 7699 Å.

Similar equipment to that used for determining sodium may also be used for determining potassium. Filter instruments with a simple red-cut-off filter, allow the use of barrier layer or photo-conductive photocells, but if a monochromator is used, a red-sensitive photomultiplier (e.g. RCA IP22) is essential as a detector. Hollow-cathode lamps may be used[61] but vapour-discharge lamps are preferred. It is sometimes possible to use a sodium-vapour lamp for determining potassium because sufficient potassium impurity may be present in the lamp to cause emission of the potassium resonance lines.[46] Low current operation of the lamp, thereby reducing self absorption and line broadening, is necessary in order to obtain maximum sensitivity, and some means is essential for separating the absorbed light from that emitted from the flame (cf. page 20).

The majority of elements do not seriously interfere with the determination of potassium. David[54] states that phosphate, aluminium, sulphate and silicate, at levels of up to forty times that of potassium, cause no interference. Willis found that calcium, magnesium and phosphorus in the proportions normally found in blood serum, had no effect on the determination of potassium but, in the presence of sodium, an enhancement in the measured absorption was obtained. In addition, the type of flame used was shown to influence the concentration of potassium atoms. Maximum sensitivity was obtained in cool flames; this observation, together with the known effect of sodium, is in accordance with the work of Foster and Hume[38] who demonstrated that the degree of ionization of potassium was dependent both on the temperature of the flame and the presence of other easily ionized atoms, for example, sodium.

Malmstadt and Chambers[62] observed that up to a twenty-fold excess of sodium did not interfere with the potassium determination. This statement appears to be in direct conflict with the evidence of Willis, particularly because Malmstadt and Chambers used an air/propane flame, which is hotter than the air/coal-gas flame in which Willis detected interference from sodium.

Regarding the relative value of atomic-absorption and emission flame-photometric methods, comments made earlier (page 89) relative to sodium apply equally to potassium. Absorption measurements are preferable to filter flame-photometric procedures, because of the elimination of spectral interference, but all other forms of interference are common to both procedures.

The higher sensitivity of emission methods, particularly when a monochromator is used for wavelength selection, is usually sufficient to justify emission flame-photometry rather than atomic-absorption spectrophotometry as a means for determining this particular element.

CHAPTER 14

COPPER

THE determination of copper in a variety of agricultural materials is described by Allan.[65]

Several lines in the copper spectrum may be used for absorption measurements, the most sensitive being 3247 Å, for which a limit of detection of 0·1 ppm can be achieved. Several copper lines in the vicinity of the zinc line at 2138 Å may also be used for absorption measurements; these lines were responsible for the absorption detected by Gidley and Jones[29] when hydrochloric acid was sprayed through a brass burner. An explanation for the apparent interference on zinc was subsequently reported by the same authors[47] as being due to dissolution of corrosion products from the interior surface of the brass burner used.

An increase in sensitivity may be achieved by using low hollow-cathode lamp currents, due to the narrowing of the emission spectrum lines. No increase in sensitivity, however, can be obtained by using high-temperature flames, because copper exists almost entirely in the atomic state at the temperature of conventional air/coal-gas flames; in practice, a cooler flame is preferred, because expansion of the flame gases is less and hence the concentration of atoms/unit volume is greater in the cooler flame. Like many other elements, sensitivity of the method may be increased by using an organic reagent, and Allan, in a further paper[33] gives details of experiments designed to establish the cause of enhancement due to the presence of various organic reagents. The major cause of enhancement was shown to be due to an increase in the concentration of droplets reaching the flame achieved by the greater efficiency of atomization. The effect of organic reagents on an air/acetylene flame, with an indirect atomizer, was to reduce the flame temerpature, and one result of this is the production of an increased concentration of atoms, resulting from the smaller expansion of flame gases in the cooler flame. A combination of the calculated effects due to these two causes of enhancement, agrees very well with experimental observations. Smaller enhancements can be achieved by adding a miscible organic reagent but, in practice, the advantage of this increase in sensitivity is offset by the increased dilution of the sample with the organic reagent (cf. General Considerations, page 26).

Allan describes applications of a method to the analysis of a variety of agricultural materials, some of which are applied direct to aqueous solutions, but in others, where high sensitivity is required, copper is first reacted with ammonium pyrrolidine dithiocarbamate and the complex is extracted into an immiscible organic reagent; details of methods for the analysis of fertilizers, soils, soil extracts and plants are given. Although no comparisons are given of results obtained by atomic-absorption and alternative procedures, Allan indicates that the method is accurate and free from interferences, because of the concordance of results obtained from different sized samples and the completeness of his recoveries.

Further evidence of accuracy and freedom from interference has been obtained in the authors' laboratory. A one hundredfold excess of ten of the more common elements (including silicon) had no effect on the absorption due to copper. Applications to the analysis of aluminium and zinc alloys is simple and the method may also be used for the determination of residual copper in the electrolyte after electrodeposition of copper has taken place. The possible wide range of composition of trade effluents also has no effect on the determination of copper in these samples.

CHAPTER 15

CADMIUM

REFERENCE has been made to the high sensitivity of detection of cadmium,[8, 11] but no papers appear to have been published giving details of any analytical applications.

In a limited amount of work in the authors' laboratory, it has been found that, using the most sensitive line Cd 2288 Å, a limit of detection of 0·07 ppm can be obtained; a cadmium hollow-cathode lamp operating at 5 mA, as a sharp line source, was used. A low lamp current is essential in order to avoid melting of the cathode material, and is an advantage in giving increased absorption.

Cadmium is completely dissociated to atoms in a cool air/coal-gas flame and no interferences were recorded due to the presence of hydrochloric, nitric or sulphuric acids, except those normally attributed to variation in physical properties of the solution. Similar effects to those reported for zinc (page 50) were observed when cation interferences were investigated. When twelve of the more common elements were examined, only silicon affected the absorption significantly. Concentrated solutions caused a reduction in atomizer efficiency—an effect readily circumvented by using standards of comparable concentration.

Even though the method is highly sensitive, it may not be sufficient for some determinations, e.g. in the analysis of certain nuclear-engineering materials, where limits of 0·5 ppm cadmium are frequently imposed. An increase in sensitivity can be obtained by extracting cadmium into an organic solvent, which is subsequently sprayed into the flame. Using such a method a procedure has been developed in the authors' laboratory, when a simple dithizone-extraction into iso-butyl methyl ketone has enabled a detection limit of 0·1 ppm cadmium, in zirconium, to be obtained; this extraction also permits lead and zinc to be determined in the same sample, because the same organic extract can be used for these additional determinations. In this way, the limits of detection for lead and zinc, are extended to 5 and 0·1 ppm respectively (calculated on the solid sample).

CHAPTER 16

OTHER ELEMENTS

ALTHOUGH many elements, other than those already described, may be detected by atomic-absorption methods, little, if any, information regarding analytical applications has been published (see Table 4).

Lockyer and Hames[13] showed that silver, gold, platinum, rhodium and palladium may be detected, using the Hilger, Atomic-Absorption Attachment; the limits of detection are given in Table 13.

TABLE 13.

DETECTION LIMITS

Element	Limit of detection (ppm)*
Silver	0·25
Gold	1
Platinum	10
Rhodium	1
Palladium	2

*Based on optical density of 0·005.

No mutual interferences were detected between these elements, but it was found necessary to oxidize any iron present in solution, in order to avoid precipitation of metallic gold. It was also found necessary to use a water-cooled burner top to ensure that unstable gold salts were not decomposed to metallic gold particles before entering the flame.

Other elements have been listed as being detectable by conventional atomizer-flame methods and Table 14 lists the wavelengths of lines used (where given) and sensitivities claimed by several different workers[8, 11, 48, 66]. It is emphasized that the sensitivities quoted may not all be equivalent, because the definitions of limit of detection by different workers may not be the same.

TABLE 14.

DETECTION LIMITS

Element	Wavelength of absorption line (Å)	Limit of detection (ppm)
Antimony	2311	2
Barium	5535	10
Bismuth	3068	2
Caesium	8521	10
Chromium	3579	0·1
Cobalt	2407	0·2
Gallium	2874	3
Lithium	6708	1
Mercury	2536	10
Molybdenum	3133	0·5
Nickel	3415	0·2
Rubidium	7800	2
Strontium	5535	0·1
Thallium	2767	1
Tin	2863	5

A useful and comprehensive list of detection limits has been given by Gatehouse and Willis[66] in a paper describing the performance of a simple atomic-absorption spectrophotometer.

REFERENCES

(1) MILBOURN, M. and GIDLEY, J. A. F., *J. Inst. Met.*, **86**, 219 (1958).
(2) PROKOF'EV, V. F., *C. R. Acad. Sci.*, U.R.S.S., **29**, 443 (1940).
(3) WALSH, A., *Spectrochimica Acta*, **7**, 108 (1955).
(4) KING, R. B. and STOCKBARGER, D. C., *Astrophys. J.*, **91**, 488 (1940).
(5) MITCHELL, A. C. G. and ZEMANSKY, M. W., *Resonance Radiation and Excited Atoms*, Cambridge University Press, 1934.
(6) MENZIES, A. C., *Anal. Chem.*, **32**, 898 (1960).
(7) TOLANSKY, S., *Proc. Roy. Soc.* A, **137**, 541 (1932).
(8) RUSSELL, B. J., SHELTON, J. P. and Walsh, A., *Spectrochimica Acta*, **8**, 317 (1947).
(9) MEGGERS, W. F. and WESTFALL, F. O., *J. Res. Nat. Bur. Standards*, **44**, 447 (1950).
(10) ZELIKOFF, M., WYCKOFF, P. H., ASCHENBRAND, L. M. and LOOMIS, R. S., *J. Opt. Soc. Amer.*, **42**, 818 (1952).
(11) e.g. Hilger and Watts Ltd., London, Catalogue CH.407, 1959 and Perkin-Elmer Corporation, Connecticut.
(12) ALLAN, J. E., *Analyst*, **83**, 466 (1958).
(13) LOCKYER, R. and HAMES, G. E., *Analyst*, **84**, 385 (1959).
(14) DAVID, D. J., *Analyst*, **83**, 655 (1958).
(15) RUSSELL, B. J. and WALSH, A., *Spectrochimica Acta*, **15**, 883 (1959).
(16) TOLANSKY, S., *High-Resolution Spectroscopy*, p. 19 ff. Methuen, London, 1957.
(17) DIEKE, G. H. and CROSSWHITE, H. M., *J. Opt. Soc. Amer.*, **42**, 433 (1952).
(18) CROSSWHITE, H. M., DIEKE, G. H. and LEGAGNEUR, C. S., *J. Opt. Soc. Amer.*, **45**, 270 (1955).
(19) JONES, W. G. and WALSH, A., *Spectrochimica Acta*, **16**, 249 (1960).
(20) LOCKYER, R., *Hilger Journal*, **5**, 55 (1959).
(21) HULDT, L. and LAGERQUIST, A., *Arkiv. Fysik.*, **2**, 333 (1950).
(22) BAKER, M. R. and VALLEE, B. L., *J. Opt. Soc. Amer.*, **45**, 773 (1955).
(23) MARGOSHES, M. and SCRIBNER, B. F., *Spectrochimica Acta*, **15**, 138 (1959).
(24) GATEHOUSE, B. M. and WALSH, A., *Spectrochimica Acta*, **16**, 602 (1960).
(25) WHITE, J. U., *J. Opt. Soc. Amer.*, **32**, 285 (1942).
(26) DAVID, D. J., *Analyst*, **84**, (1959).
(27) ALLAN, J. E., *Spectrochimica Acta*, **15**, 800 (1959).
(28) NAISH, J. M. and RAMSDEN, W., *Spectrochimica Acta*, **5**, 295 (1952).
(29) GIDLEY, J. A. F. and JONES, J. T., *Analyst*, **85**, 249 (1960).
(30) BOX, G. F. and WALSH, A., *Spectrochimica Acta*, **16**, 255 (1960).
(31) ROBINSON, J. W., *Anal. Chim. Acta.*, **23**, 458 (1960).
(32) MENZIES, A. C., Lecture to Applied Spectroscopy Group of the Institute of Physics and Physical Society (London) December 1960.

[33] ALLAN, J. E., *Spectrochimica Acta*, **17**, 467 (1961).

[34] LOCKYER, R., SCOTT, J. E. and SLADE, S., *Nature*, **189**, 830 (1961).

[35] ROBINSON, J. W., *Anal. Chim. Acta*, **23**, 479 (1960).

[36] BAKER, C. A., Lectures to Physical Methods Group of the Society for Analytical Chemistry (May and November 1960), private communication, and BAKER, C. A. and GARTON, F. W. J., U.K.A.E.A., Report A.E.R.E., R3490 (1961)

[37] WILLIS, J. B., *Spectrochimica Acta*, **16**, 259 (1960).

[38] FOSTER, W. H. and HUME, D. N., *Anal. Chem.*, **31**, 2033 (1959).

[39] DAVIS, H. M., FOX, G. P., WEBB, R. J. and WILDY, P. C., U.K.A.E.A., Report, A.E.R.E. C/R2659.

[40] CLINTON, O. E., *Spectrochimica Acta*, **16**, 985 (1960).

[41] SCHATZ, F. V., *J. Inst. Metals*, **80**, 77 (1951).

[42] SUTCLIFFE, G. R. and PEAKE, D. M., private communication.

[43] ROSSELAND, *Theoretical Astrophysics*, Clarendon Press, Oxford, 1936.

[44] WOODSON, *Rev. Sci. Instr.*, **10**, 308 (1939).

[45] MENZIES, A. C., XV Congresso Internacional De Quimica Pura E Aplicada (Quimica Analitica) IV-37 Lisbon 1958.

[46] CARR-BRION, K. G., private communication.

[47] GIDLEY, J. A. F. and JONES, J. T., *Analyst*, **86**, 271 (1961).

[48] ROBINSON, J. W., *Anal. Chem.*, **32**, 17A (1960).

[49] ELWELL, W. T. and GIDLEY, J. A. F., *Anal. Chim. Acta.*, **24**, 71 (1961).

[50] ROBINSON, J. W., *Anal. Chim. Acta*, **24**, 451 (1961).

[51] WILLIS, J. B., *Spectrochimica Acta*, **16**, 273 (1960).

[52] MITCHELL, R. L. and ROBERTSON, I. M., *J. Soc. Chem. Ind.*, **55**, 269T (1936).

[53] FUKUSHIMA, S., SHIGEMOTO, M., KATO, I. and OTOZAI, K., *Mikrochim. Acta*, 135 (1957).

[54] DAVID, D. J., *Analyst*, **85**, 495 (1960).

[55] WILLIS, J. B., *Nature*, **186**, 249 (1960). *Ibid.*, **184**, 186 (1959).

[56] WILLIS, J. B., *Anal. Chem.*, **33**, 556 (1961).

[57] MacINTYRE, I., *Biochem. J.*, **67**, 164 (1957).

[58] STRASHEIM, A. and NELL, J. P., *J. S. African Chem. Inst.*, **7**, 79 (1954).

[59] DEAN, J. A., *Flame Photometry*, McGraw-Hill, 1960, pp. 280-283.

[60] Idem *Ibid.*, p. 197.

[61] WILLIS, J. B., *Spectrochimica Acta*, **16**, 551 (1960).

[62] MALMSTADT, H. V. and CHAMBERS, W. E., *Anal. Chem*, **32**, 225 (1960).

[63] BROWNHILL, P., Second Australian Spectroscopy Conference, June, 1959 (see *Nature*, **184**, 1197, 1959).

[64] C.S.I.R.O. Industrial Research News, No. 17, September 1959.

[65] ALLAN, J. E., *Spectrochimica Acta*, **17**, 459 (1961).

[66] GATEHOUSE, B. M., and WILLIS, J. B., *Spectrochimica Acta*, **17**, 710 (1961).

SUBJECT INDEX

101